13 May — 12 Jun

RUNNING WILD

by **MICHAEL MORPURGO**
in an adaptation by **SAMUEL ADAMSON**

15 Jul — 27 Aug

JESUS CHRIST SUPERSTAR

lyrics by **TIM RICE**   music by **ANDREW LLOYD WEBBER**

17 Jun — 09 Jul

HENRY V

by **WILLIAM SHAKESPEARE**

02 Sep — 17 Sep

PRIDE AND PREJUDICE

by **JANE AUSTEN**
in an adaptation by **SIMON READE**

REGENT'S PARK
OPEN AIR THEATRE

0844 826 4242
openairtheatre.com

THE ROYAL PARKS   **Magic**   The Telegraph

Lord of the Flies 2015. Photo David Jensen.

Hear the world's best in the world's best acoustics

Still to come this season:

Mark Padmore and Paul Lewis perform Schubert's Schwanengesang

Dame Mitsuko Uchida, Igor Levitt and Murray Perahia in recital

Moscow State Symphony Orchestra perform Shostakovich's Symphony No 5

Daniel Hope celebrates Yehudi Menuhin's centenary

Sir Andras Schiff with the Chamber Orchestra of Europe

Edward Gardner conducts National Youth Orchestra of Great Britain

Follow us

f **Town Hall Symphony Hall**

@THSHBirmingham

townhallsymphonyhall

thsh_birmingham

Box office
0121 780 3333
www.thsh.co.uk

THSH
TOWN HALL BIRMINGHAM   SYMPHONY HALL BIRMINGHAM

© Decca / Justin Pumfrey

JOIN US FOR OUR YEAR-ROUND FESTIVAL OF MUSIC

Mandela Trilogy © John Snelling

Vladimir Jurowski © Richard Cannon

Arabella Steinbacher© Peter Rigaud

MANDELA TRILOGY
Cape Town Opera's epic tribute to an icon.

BELIEF AND BEYOND BELIEF FESTIVAL
World class musicians explore life,
the universe and everything in between.

FILM SCORES LIVE SERIES
Hear iconic soundtracks to movie classics
including *Psycho* and *Vertigo*.

INTERNATIONAL ORCHESTRA SERIES
Featuring Martha Argerich,
Budapest Festival Orchestra and Les Siècles.

RESIDENT ORCHESTRAS
London Philharmonic Orchestra
The full Sibelius Symphony Cycle in four concerts.

Philharmonia Orchestra
Delve into the music of Beethoven and Boulez.

Orchestra of the Age of Enlightenment
Take a journey into unusual French repertoire.

London Sinfonietta
The best music of the 21st century.

SOUTHBANKCENTRE.CO.UK/CLASSICAL
0844 847 9934

THE HOME OF CLASSICAL MUSIC

SOUTHBANK CENTRE

LOTTERY FUNDED

Supported using public funding by
ARTS COUNCIL ENGLAND

£5 tickets for Under 35s at Wigmore Hall

www.wigmore-hall.org.uk/u35

WIGMORE HALL

'I think the impact is much greater in a direct performance scenario... it's exciting and fun, and you never quite know what is going to happen!'
Anna Sideris, young audience member

'When performers open up and release that barrier... that's when the magic happens.'
Rannveig Káradóttir, young audience member

Buy a ticket to selected concerts throughout the season for just £5!

John Mark Ainsley | Benjamin Grosvenor | Hagen Quartet | Louis Lortie
Sophie Bevan | Isabelle Faust | Kuss Quartet | Llŷr Williams | Christoph Prégardien
Marlis Petersen | Borodin Quartet | Florian Boesch | Sarah Connolly | Julia Fischer
Kristian Bezuidenhout | Ann Murray DBE | Heath Quartet | James Baillieu | Lars Vogt
Marc-André Hamelin | Miah Persson | Elias String Quartet | Mahan Esfahani
and many more!

DIRECTOR: JOHN GILHOOLY OBE
36 WIGMORE STREET, LONDON W1U 2BP
REGISTERED CHARITY NO. 1024838

Department for Culture Media & Sport | LOTTERY FUNDED | Supported using public funding by ARTS COUNCIL ENGLAND

Photograph © Benjamin Ealovega

TRINITY LABAN CONSERVATOIRE
OF MUSIC & DANCE

PROFESSIONAL TRAINING FOR CREATIVE MUSICIANS

TRINITYLABAN.AC.UK f 🐦 You Tube /TRINITYLABAN

BBC PROMS 2016 AT A GLANCE

75 PROMS
AT THE ROYAL ALBERT HALL

Performances from leading international orchestras, artists
and conductors:

58 MAIN EVENING CONCERTS

9 LATE NIGHT PROMS After-hours adventures – from Bach
to Bowie and from Brazilian dance rhythms to gospel sounds

8 MATINEES Including Ten Pieces II, CBeebies and the
Simón Bolívar Symphony Orchestra

PLUS 8 PROMS EXTRA LATES Free after-hours music
and poetry featuring bright new talent, with a late bar

76 PROMS EXTRA EVENTS AT THE IMPERIAL COLLEGE UNION

A festival in itself: free workshops, talks and participation events – plus a new series of archive performances on film

8 PROMS CHAMBER MUSIC
AT CADOGAN HALL

World-class chamber music and song

4 'PROMS AT ...'

Concerts matching music to four exciting venues:
Bold Tendencies Multi-Storey Car Park, Peckham;
Old Royal Naval College, Greenwich; Roundhouse,
Camden; Sam Wanamaker Playhouse

BBC RADIO

Every Prom live
on BBC Radio 3;
collaborations with
BBC Radio 2 and 6 Music

BBC TV First and Last
nights; Fridays and Sundays
(BBC Four); Saturdays
during the Olympic Games
(BBC Two); plus weekly
Proms Extra hosted by
Katie Derham (BBC Two)

BBC ONLINE

Listen/watch again for
30 days after broadcast
and explore curated clips
on the BBC Proms website

ENGLAND,
N. IRELAND, SCOTLAND
& WALES

Last Night of the Proms celebrations
in the Royal Albert Hall and at
Proms in the Park events around the UK

BBC Proms 2016

THE BBC PRESENTS THE 122ND SEASON OF HENRY WOOD PROMENADE CONCERTS, BROADCASTING EVERY PROM LIVE ON BBC RADIO 3

Director, BBC Proms David Pickard
Controller, BBC Radio 3 Alan Davey
Personal Assistant Yvette Pusey

Editor, BBC Radio 3 Emma Bloxham

Head of Marketing, Publications and Learning Kate Finch

Proms & Live Events Helen Heslop (Manager), Hannah Donat, Alys Jones (Producers), Adele Conlin, Holly Cumming (Co-ordinators)

Press & Communications Camilla Dervan (Communications Manager), Victoria Taylor (Assistant Publicist), Shari Rautenbach (Publicity Assistant)

Marketing Emily Caket (Manager), Julia McGill (Assistant)

Learning Ellara Wakely (Senior Learning Manager), Melanie Fryer, Garth McArthur (Managers), Rebecca Burns, Lauren Creed, Naomi Selwyn (Co-ordinators), Catherine Humphrey (Administrator)

Business Co-ordinator Tricia Twigg

Music Television Mark Cooper (Head of Music Television, London), Francesca Kemp (Executive Producer), Michael Ledger (Series Production Manager)

Digital Andrew Caspari (Head of Speech Radio and Classical Music Multiplatform), Andrew Downs (BBC Proms Digital Editorial Lead), Rhian Roberts (Digital Editor, BBC Radio 3)

BBC Music Library Natalie Dewar (Senior Media Manager), Emma MacDonald (Team Leader), Declan Kennedy (Proms Librarian), Tim Auvache, David Beaman, Anne Butcher, Rachel Davis, Raymond Howden, Alison John, Richard Malton, Claire Martin, Rebecca Nye, Giovanni Quaglia, Paul Turner

Business Affairs Emma Trevelyan (Head of Business Affairs), Mark Waring (Manager), Sue Dickson, Hilary Dodds, Kate Foreman, Maddie Hennessy, Annie Kelly, Simon Launchbury, Pamela Wise (Executives)

Publications Editor Petra Abbam
Editorial Manager Edward Bhesania
Sub-Editor Úna-Frances Clarke
Publications Designer Joanna Robbins
Publications Assistant Deborah Fether
Junior Designer Niamh Richardson

Advertising John Good Ltd
Cover illustration D8.
Published by BBC Proms Publications, Room 1045, Broadcasting House, London W1A 1AA
Distributed by BBC Books, an imprint of Ebury Publishing, a Random House Group Company, 20 Vauxhall Bridge Road, London SW1V 2SA

Printed by APS Group
APS Group holds ISO 14001 environmental management, FSC and PEFC accreditations. Printed using vegetable-based inks on FSC-certified paper.
Formed in 1993 as a response to concerns over global deforestation, FSC (Forest Stewardship Council) is an independent, non-governmental, not-for-profit organisation established to promote the responsible management of the world's forests. For more information, please visit www.fsc-uk.org.

FSC
www.fsc.org
MIX
Paper from
responsible sources
FSC® C003270

ISBN 978-1785940491

BBC MUSIC

BBC RADIO 3

BBC PROMS GUIDE 2016 CONTENTS

**THIS GUIDE IS
ALSO AVAILABLE
AS AN APP!**

Fully optimised for
iOS and Android on
mobile and tablet –
download the new
Proms Guide app from
app stores for £2.99

STAY INFORMED facebook.com/theproms @bbcproms (#bbcproms) or sign up for our newsletter: bbc.co.uk/proms

THE PROMS 1895–2016

The scale and range of the Proms have changed dramatically over the 121 years since the first season, but founder-conductor Henry Wood's original vision of making the best music available to the widest possible audience still sustains the Proms today

The BBC Symphony Orchestra performing against the luxuriant palm-tree backdrop of the Queen's Hall stage

BEYOND THE QUEEN'S HALL

The Queen's Hall in London's Langham Place was home to the Proms from 1895 until 1941, when it was gutted by fire after being bombed in an air raid. That year the festival moved to the Royal Albert Hall, which has since hosted over 4,300 Proms concerts. In 1971, for the first time, three Proms took place away from the RAH, at the Royal Opera House, Westminster Cathedral and the Roundhouse, and a selection of Proms in alternative venues continued for a further two decades. That tradition is revived this season, with Proms taking place once again at the Roundhouse, as well as the Sam Wanamaker Playhouse, the Old Royal Naval College, Greenwich, and a multi-storey car park in Peckham. The first Proms Chamber Music series took place in 1996, finding a regular home at Cadogan Hall since 2005.

PROMS PRINCIPALS

Henry Wood conducted the Proms almost single-handedly throughout its first 50 years; other conductors such as John Barbirolli, Adrian Boult, Basil Cameron and Malcolm Sargent made regular appearances from the 1940s. The newly formed BBC Symphony Orchestra replaced the Queen's Hall Orchestra as the festival's resident ensemble in 1930, three years after the BBC took over the running of the Proms, but it was not until 1966 that the first non-British orchestra – the Moscow Radio Orchestra, under Gennady Rozhdestvensky – performed at the Proms. Visiting international ensembles have since become a feature of the season and, in 2014, more than ever were welcomed at the Proms, from such diverse countries as Australia, China, Greece, Iceland, South Korea and Qatar.

A portrait of Henry Wood by Leslie Ward (1851–1922), which appeared in *Vanity Fair* magazine in 1907

BBC (Queen's Hall); Lebrecht Music & Arts (Wood)

NOTEWORTHY PERFORMANCES

In early Proms seasons, Mondays were devoted principally to music by Wagner and Fridays were Beethoven nights. The Proms continues to increase in scope and size and give audiences the opportunity to hear the world's leading artists and ensembles. The first complete opera was heard at the Proms in 1961: Mozart's *Don Giovanni*, performed by Glyndebourne Festival Opera. Evgeny Kissin gave the first Proms solo recital in the RAH in 1997; a series of solo Bach performances featured last year. The exuberant Venezuelan forces of Gustavo Dudamel and the Simón Bolívar Symphony Orchestra danced onto the Proms stage in 2007 and they return this season; John Wilson and his hand-picked orchestra have added star-studded entertainment every year since 2009; and Doctor Who and his TARDIS first landed at the Proms in 2008.

A performance of John Cage's *Branches*, celebrating the composer's centenary in 2012, filled the Royal Albert Hall stage with cactuses

The 2014 world premiere of Benedict Mason's *Meld*, which explored the relationship between performers and space, placing musicians all around the Royal Albert Hall

CELEBRATING NEW MUSIC

Henry Wood gave the world, UK or London premieres of more than 100 British works between 1900 and 1910 and premiered many more by other composers. When William Glock became Director of the Proms in 1960, with the promise 'to re-interpret the Proms in the spirit of Sir Henry Wood', audiences were presented with music that had never before been heard in Britain, including the first electronic tape music performance at the Proms, Berio's *Perspectives*, and the first BBC commission for the Proms, Alwyn's *Derby Day*. The Proms commitment to new music continues to this day, with recent notable commissions from composers including Sir Harrison Birtwistle, Sir James MacMillan and Judith Weir.

BRINGING THE PROMS TO YOU

The first radio broadcast of a Prom was in 1932 and 15 years later, in 1947, every Prom was broadcast on radio for the first time, on the BBC's Third Programme, and the Last Night of the Proms was broadcast on TV. The Proms went digital on BBC Four in 2002 and on-demand listening also began online. Today, every Prom is broadcast live on Radio 3 and you can listen online in HD Sound. Since 2010 details of all Proms performances since 1895 have been available on the BBC Proms website and the BBC Proms Guide app – with search and calendar functions – was introduced last year.

'The Man with the Mike': TV presenter Robert Beatty (*far right*) at the Proms in 1955

Chris Christodoulou/BBC (*Meld, Branches*); BBC (*Robert Beatty*)

WELCOME TO THE 2016 BBC PROMS

It is a great pleasure, and hugely exciting, to welcome you to the 2016 BBC Proms – the 122nd year of this great festival and my first as its Director. I look forward to building on the legacy of my distinguished predecessors and to bringing you, in the founding spirit of the festival, the broadest range of classical music, performed to the very highest standard.

Since I took on this new role, many people have told me about their memories of the Proms. Often the Proms has represented their first contact with classical music, kindling a lifelong love of live performance. Individual concerts stand out in people's minds as moments of inspiration and joy. With the Proms it's personal – and that's just how I feel about them.

The first Prom I ever attended, as a teenager, was a performance of Mahler's *Das Lied von der Erde* featuring a young conductor called Andrew Davis, and the leading mezzo-soprano of the day, Janet Baker. In a happy coincidence the same work appears in this year's Proms, and how heartening it is that (now Sir) Andrew – having nurtured a long association with the BBC Symphony Orchestra – has a regular presence here. When, last year, I Prommed up in the Royal Albert Hall's Gallery, I was also reassured to find that the unique atmosphere of informality and concentration has continued to flourish in the past four decades.

While I have been a regular Proms-goer for some 40 years, my professional association

DB (illustration); Thane BurgkBerg/BBC (Pickard)

with the BBC Proms began over 20 years ago, first as Chief Executive of the Orchestra of the Age of Enlightenment and then as General Director of Glyndebourne. Now I enter the next, and most personal, phase of my relationship with the Proms, and set out, with you, on a further journey of exploration.

So where might this journey take us? Well, this year we will be exploring some new spaces for Proms concerts. As well as being a national and international festival, the Proms is also central to the cultural life of London. So, in addition to our regular homes at the Royal Albert Hall and Cadogan Hall, this year we are taking four Saturday matinees to further venues around the city, with each concert matching music to the setting. So there are Shakespeare-inspired works by Purcell at Shakespeare's Globe, Rossini's *Petite messe solennelle* in the beautiful Chapel of the Old Royal Naval College, Greenwich, and Steve Reich at a multi-storey car park in Peckham. And, in a year in which we mourn the death of that great pioneer Pierre Boulez, I can think of no better time for the Proms to return to the Roundhouse in Camden – the scene of a series of memorable concerts in the 1970s and early 1980s, not least those directed by Boulez himself during his time as Chief Conductor

The Ten Pieces Choir at last year's Ten Pieces Proms: this year the focus turns from primary-school to secondary-school pupils (Proms 10 & 12)

of the BBC SO. I hope that each venue will add a new dimension to the concert experience.

With the 400th anniversary this year of the death of our greatest playwright, William Shakespeare, we sample some of the extraordinary range of music that he has inspired, including not just key works of the orchestral repertoire, such as Tchaikovsky's three Shakespeare-inspired overtures, but also less familiar pieces by composers including Hans Abrahamsen, Debussy, Jonathan Dove, Fauré and Richard Rodgers.

Other anniversaries and birthdays we mark this year include those of Henri Dutilleux, Colin Matthews, Anthony Payne, Steve Reich and Erik Satie, and we celebrate the 50th anniversary of Bernard Haitink's first Proms appearance with a performance of Mahler's Symphony No. 3 – with the great Dutch conductor aptly returning to a composer he has tirelessly championed in his long and distinguished career.

Following last year's celebration of the piano concerto, we focus this year on the cello, with no fewer than 10 cello concertos (four of them world or London premieres) and a multiple-cellos Proms Chamber Music concert led by Guy Johnston. We also make a special feature of Rossini this summer and, in the year in which the Olympics are staged in Brazil, we throw a spotlight on the music and artists of South America.

A vital part of the Proms mission is to bring classical music to new audiences. Key to this task is our hugely ambitious Learning programme, which drives a range of initiatives – including two Proms devoted to the BBC's Ten Pieces II project, a reinvention of the

Clockwise from top left: Martha Argerich (Prom 43), Narek Hakhnazaryan (Prom 47), Sir Simon Rattle (Proms 64 & 66) and Simone Young (Prom 62)

CBeebies Proms that were such a success in 2013, and a series of weekend matinee concerts aimed specifically at family audiences. This year I am especially looking forward to a concert introduced by Tom Service in which he takes apart and reconstructs the repertoire in a way that is fascinating for curious minds of all ages.

And it's not just listening that will bring new audiences to classical music, it's also participation. Events such as our Proms Extra Sing or Proms Family Orchestra sessions – which invite people of all musical abilities to get involved – the focus on youth ensembles in our main concert series and the huge success of our Proms Youth Choir, all show how taking part can genuinely change lives. I hope we can develop this participation still further in the future. It is a sign of the increasing importance of this work that the Proms Youth Ensemble, formed last year, is playing a new work in the

The Proms marks the 400th anniversary of the death of William Shakespeare with music spanning more than three centuries, ranging from Purcell to Hans Abrahamsen

Last Night of the Proms, composed by an alumnus of our Inspire competition for young composers, Tom Harrold.

At the heart of the Proms are the sheer variety of artists and ensembles involved and the range of music they play. The core of the orchestral contribution comes from the five BBC orchestras, and we also feature a thrilling array of some of the finest orchestras from around the world, including such illustrious ensembles as the Berlin Philharmonic, Budapest Festival Orchestra, Leipzig Gewandhaus Orchestra, São Paulo Symphony Orchestra, Simón Bolívar Symphony Orchestra, Berlin Staatskapelle, Dresden Staatskapelle and West–Eastern Divan Orchestra.

Soloists include not only established international stars but also a strong showing of exciting emerging talents, with no fewer than 15 current or former members of BBC Radio 3's New Generation Artists scheme and, on the Last Night of the Proms, 16 solo singers who represent the cream of today's finest young voices. Over more than 120 years the Proms has introduced audiences to the latest works by Bax, Delius, Elgar, Schoenberg and others. This year we present a total of 15 world premieres as well as a number of other works by living composers which enjoy well-deserved repeat performances that will help to establish them as part of the core repertoire.

Central to the Proms commitment to making classical music accessible to all is the availability of up to 1,350 Promming tickets for every performance, which – even with an increase in price to £6 (the first in 10 years) – remain an astonishing bargain. All of this, of course, is supplemented by the huge additional audience we reach through the variety of BBC platforms, whether it be live coverage of every concert on BBC Radio 3, the wide range of concerts and other programmes on BBC Television, or the performances available to watch online. With the increasing opportunities to watch or listen online in your own time, there have never been more ways to engage with the Proms.

It is only through the support of the BBC – via you, the licence-fee payers – that we are able to produce such a wealth of music-making and broadcasting and with such low ticket prices. I look forward to seeing you at the 2016 BBC Proms. However you encounter this remarkable festival, I hope that we will continue to serve, challenge and delight you, our huge, diverse and much-valued audience. ●

David Pickard
Director, BBC Proms

WELCOME FROM ALAN DAVEY CONTROLLER, BBC RADIO 3

A very warm welcome to the BBC Proms 2016, for the first time under the artistic directorship of David Pickard. The Proms is the most democratic classical music festival in the world and central to BBC Radio 3 and our mission to connect audiences with great music and culture. Radio 3 is proud to broadcast every Prom – on air and online in HD Sound – and to bring you the magic of the Proms wherever you are. Hear every Prom from the best seat in the house, live and available not only on-demand but also to download for 30 days.

Complementing the superb visiting orchestras and musicians from all over the world, the BBC's own brilliant Performing Groups – five orchestras, two choruses and the BBC Singers – form the backbone of the Proms programme. You can see and hear them all year round, live and on BBC Radio 3, bringing world-class performances and adventurous programming that form a key part of music-making in this country.

I am particularly pleased that this year's Proms will see the return of the Proms Youth Choir and the Proms Youth Ensemble – giving young musicians the chance to play on the world stage that the Proms offers.

Throughout the programme you will also encounter current and former BBC Radio 3 New Generation Artists – another example of how Radio 3 and BBC Music are investing in talent and the wider musical ecology.

In these busy summer months the Proms brings you the best of music from the UK and around the world – come and join us on Radio 3 the rest of the year, where the exploration continues.

BBC Concert ORCHESTRA

Inspiring musical experiences

Hear us on BBC Radio 2's Friday Night Is Music Night. Listen out for us on soundtracks, both on television and the big screen. Get involved at one of our learning events. Join us as we search out the unusual and quirky, and profile classical masterpieces on BBC Radio 3.

Highlights

27 November 2016
Total Immersion:
Richard Rodney Bennett
Murder on the Orient Express
and jazz sounds from the eclectic
master of multiple genres

25 February 2017
Music to Die For
Exploring death and spirituality
in popular culture through music
for film and theatre

19 March 2017
From Heaven to Hell at the
Movies – Sound of Cinema Live
A heavenly journey through some
of the greatest choral moments
from the big screen

@bbcco
facebook.com/bbcconcertorchestra
bbc.co.uk/concertorchestra

ASSOCIATE AT
SOUTHBANK
CENTRE
The home of classical music

MY PROMS

Katie Derham introduces a series in which five celebrities share their memories of the Proms, revealing the effect of first encounters with key pieces, the atmosphere of the Royal Albert Hall and what they're looking forward to this year

There is something very special about the Proms – something I've never experienced at any other festival or concert. A history of excellence reassures any Prommer that what they're going to see will be not just good but great, even if it is unexpected. Soloists take chances. Conductors push orchestras to new heights. And all of this happens in a venue that encourages music-lovers of all types and all ages to relax and enjoy the magic together – in a rather friendly, low-key kind of way, despite the breathtaking architecture. Respectful, but convivial at the same time. Your jaw may be dropping as you look up at the dome of the Royal Albert Hall but nobody minds if you have come straight from the park in your shorts and flip-flops.

Of course, I'm unbelievably lucky. Presenting the Proms broadcasts for radio and television, I not only get a cracking seat for the performances but I also see the musicians backstage and hear them in rehearsal. On *Proms Extra* on Saturdays on BBC Two during the season, I interview the most exciting performers and composers in the world, all of whom talk about the very special atmosphere in the Hall. And all of them say that the atmosphere is down to the audience. When there are 6,000 of us rapt and silent at the end of a ravishing work, it is the best silence in the world: it feels intimate, they say, as if they're playing a small chamber concert, almost a private gig, despite the cavernous space.

This year, as always, I feel spoilt for choice. With 75 concerts to choose from – plus others at Cadogan Hall and, this season, at other venues around London – it's easy for the eye to be dazzled by the big names: the Rattles and Dudamels, the Barenboims and Wilsons. I'm excited by the focus on cello concertos this year, starting with Sol Gabetta playing Elgar's concerto on the First Night. I'm intrigued to hear the City of Birmingham Symphony Orchestra under its dynamic young music-director-to-be, Lithuanian Mirga Gražinytė-Tyla. With the Olympics taking place in Rio during the Proms season, it should be thrilling to hear the São Paulo Symphony Orchestra with its wonderful Principal Conductor, Marin Alsop. As a lover of Brazilian music, I'm looking forward to the Late Night Prom that follows it – a celebration of popular Brazilian music from the past 100 years. Get ready for plenty of bossa nova and some energetic samba-dancing in the Arena!

It won't come as any surprise, though, to learn that the Prom I'm most excited about is the Strictly Prom. After an autumn spent learning to dance, I will be able to enjoy the experience one more time and welcome the fabulous professionals from *Strictly Come Dancing* into the Royal Albert Hall, to dance to the BBC Concert Orchestra. Whatever happens, there will be music, there will be dancing, there will be sequins … •

MY PROMS

William Sharman (athlete), *p11*
'I definitely think of competing in a race as being a performance …'

Cerys Matthews (singer, broadcaster), *p39*
'It's in the DNA of the Proms that the familiar sits side by side with the new and undiscovered …'

Fiona Shaw (actor, director), *p59*
'I have great memories of rehearsing for that Prom but I do remember being awfully terrified …'

Max Richter (composer), *p83*
'Like many student composers, I was obsessed by the music of Mahler …'

Laura Mvula (singer-songwriter), *p85*
'My Late Night Prom in 2014 felt like a wedding day – I felt like I had entered a dream …'

MY PROMS
WILLIAM SHARMAN
athlete

I was at a Proms in the Park event about 10 years ago – I went with my parents and I remember the audience calling for more and more encores. It was a fabulous experience. I come from a musical family and we would often go to concerts and events together. We all play musical instruments, so it was a treat to go to a well-run, professional event and listen to popular pieces. I got into the piano – from the age of 5 – because of my dad. He played professionally, mainly as an organist, but listening to him even just playing pop songs was encouraging and inspiring, and I wanted to be able to do that too.

The training for music is harder than for athletics in my opinion and it has taught me so much discipline for competing in track and field. I have that experience of being in front of an audience, dealing with pressure and nerves – it's all very similar to what I do now as an athlete. I definitely think of competing in a race as being a performance, with all that practice leading to one particular moment. But, when I'm not travelling and doing competitions,

Training in music has taught me discipline for competing in track and field.

I spend a lot of time on the piano – I find music can also be really relaxing. It was great fun to take part in a concert at Kings Place in London earlier this year, having had the time to knock a few pieces into shape!

I used to play cornet in my school orchestra and I always loved finding out what our conductor would do with the music that we were playing, how he would add his own touch to things. One of my favourite pieces of music at the Proms is *Jerusalem*. When I represent Team England, it is played as a sort of National Anthem during our medal ceremonies. I associate the tune with achievement, so it has many fond memories for me. Whenever I hear it, it makes me feel immensely proud. ●

Favourite composer: Ravel – it's so easy to hear a romantic element in his music because it is packed with feeling.

Most recent musical 'discovery': Listening to Jack Garratt in BBC Radio 1's Live Lounge – he is an incredibly talented multi-instrumentalist and singer.

Proms 2016 highlight: Ravel's *Boléro* (Prom 4) – it's my favourite! I sometimes listen to *Boléro* before a race to try to get in the perfect state of mind. And I'm always happy to listen to anything by Mozart!

BBC NATIONAL ORCHESTRA AND CHORUS OF WALES

2016/17

Aberystwyth, Bangor, Cardiff, Cheltenham,
Llandudno, London, Newtown, St Davids, Swansea

Principal Conductor	Thomas Søndergård
Principal Guest Conductor	Xian Zhang
Conductor Laureate	Tadaaki Otaka
Composer-in-Association	Huw Watkins

bbc.co.uk/now | @bbcnow
0800 052 1812

The BBC's orchestra in the North

Performing six concerts at this year's BBC Proms.
On air on BBC Radio 3.
At home in MediaCityUK, Salford.
In residence at The Bridgewater Hall, Manchester.
Touring regionally, nationally and internationally.
Connecting with communities where they live.

Find out more, sign up for our e-newsletter, Quay Notes:
bbc.co.uk/philharmonic

Find us on: Facebook | Twitter | Instagram

BBC RADIO 3

Supported by
Salford City Council

BBC

SCOTTISH SYMPHONY ORCHESTRA
2016/17 Season

Thomas Dausgaard Chief Conductor
Ilan Volkov Principal Guest Conductor
Matthias Pintscher Artist-in-Association
John Wilson Associate Guest Conductor
Donald Runnicles Conductor Emeritus*
Laura Samuel Leader

Thomas Dausgaard Conducts:

Stravinsky's *Petrushka* and *The Rite of Spring* at the BBC Proms
Scottish Inspirations: BBC Commissions inspired by Scotland
Beethoven's 1808 Academy Concert
Bruckner's Symphony No.9 (completed version)
The Music of Rued Langgaard
Haydn's *The Creation*
Mahler's Seventh Symphony

Glasgow Season includes:

Sir Harrison Birtwistle's *The Last Supper*
Elgar Symphony Cycle
John Wilson conducts Korngold
Weill's *The Seven Deadly Sins*
Ian Bostridge sings Britten
Tectonics Festival

As well as appearances at the 2016 Edinburgh International Festival and our regular concert series in Aberdeen, Ayr, Edinburgh, Inverness and Perth.

bbc.co.uk/bbcsso

BBC RADIO 3

BBC MUSIC

BBC Scotland

*from September 2016

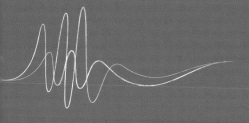

BBC SINGERS

Join the BBC Singers for a thrilling and diverse series of concerts in Milton Court Concert Hall as part of their 2016–17 season.

"...the music makes virtuosic demands, supremely well met by the BBC Singers."
The Daily Telegraph

21 OCTOBER 2016
Bach Mass in B minor

Paul Brough conductor
Susanna Hurrell soprano
Jennifer Johnston alto
Charles Daniels tenor
Mark Stone bass
St James' Baroque

13 DECEMBER 2016
BBC Singers at Christmas

A special concert for Christmas, including music by Britten, Bob Chilcott and John Rutter
Bob Chilcott conductor

19 FEBRUARY 2017
Mozart Requiem

David Hill conductor
Mary Bevan soprano
Catherine Hopper alto
Ben Johnson tenor
David Stout bass
St James' Baroque

7 JULY 2017
Alive

Choral music by Eric Whitacre and contemporaries
Eric Whitacre conductor

SINGERS AT SIX

Short concerts in St Giles' Cripplegate complementing the BBC Symphony Orchestra's Barbican Hall concerts: Rachmaninov *Vespers*, Christmas music, Bruckner and Palestrina motets and music by Czech composers.

ST PAUL'S KNIGHTSBRIDGE

Free concerts in the Victorian splendour of St Paul's Knightsbridge, featuring a wide range of glorious choral music.

Concerts in Milton Court Concert Hall
Tickets £22, £17.50, £10 – plus booking fee*

*Booking fees: £3 per transaction for online booking. £4 by phone. No fee when tickets are booked in person. Fees correct at time of going to print.

bbc.co.uk/singers
for full details of all events including our exciting learning projects and to sign up for our free e-newsletter.

@bbcsingers
facebook.com/bbcsingers

BBC RADIO 3

Broadcast on BBC Radio 3 and streamed online.

SO BBC Symphony Orchestra & Chorus

SAKARI ORAMO

Chief Conductor

Come and hear the acclaimed musical partnership
Concerts 2016–17

Concerts to excite, stimulate and delight –
from Sakari Oramo and the BBC Symphony Orchestra

Strauss *Ein Heldenleben*, Shostakovich Symphony No. 10, Sibelius
Lemminkäinen Legends, Messiaen *Turangalîla Symphony*, premieres of works
by Diana Burrell, Brett Dean, Detlev Glanert and Michael Zev Gordon.

Other season highlights:
Berlioz's *Grande messe des morts* at the Royal Albert Hall,
Death Has No Season with David Sedaris, John Adams's opera
Doctor Atomic and Neil Brand's *A Christmas Carol*.

'The BBC SO played superbly'
The Guardian

barbican

Associate
Orchestra

Box Office 020 7638 8891
barbican.org.uk

bbc.co.uk/symphonyorchestra
@bbcso facebook.com/bbcso

BBC RADIO 3

BBC Symphony Chorus

The BBC Symphony Chorus is one of the country's finest and most distinctive amateur choirs, enjoying the highest broadcast profile of any non-professional choir in the UK. It performs a wide range of exciting and challenging large-scale works in its appearances with the BBC Symphony Orchestra at the Barbican and at the BBC Proms, where it performs in a number of concerts each year.

Appearances at this year's BBC Proms include Prokofiev's *Alexander Nevsky* conducted by Sakari Oramo and the world premiere of Anthony Payne's *Of Land, Sea and Sky* with Sir Andrew Davis, as well as Mozart's Mass in C minor with the BBC Scottish Symphony Orchestra. Performances during the BBC SO's 2016–17 Barbican season include Rachmaninov's *The Bells* with Semyon Bychkov, Dvořák's *Requiem* with Jiří Bělohlávek, Berlioz's *Grande messe des morts* and music by Richard Rodney Bennett and Philip Glass.

Would you like to join us?

If you are an experienced choral singer who would like to sing new and challenging music, as well as key choral works, in a fun and friendly chorus – with leading composers in world-class venues – then the BBC Symphony Chorus could be for you!

Membership is free, and auditions for new members are held throughout the year. To find out more about us and how to audition, visit the Chorus website or contact the Chorus Administrator by email at bbcsc@bbc.co.uk or by telephone on 020 7765 4715.

bbc.co.uk/symphonychorus   @bbcso #bbcsc

POET, PLAYWRIGHT, MUSE

Whether in songs or dances, serenades or marches, Shakespeare's plays suggest music at every turn. Scholar **Stanley Wells** explores how sound permeates word and why Shakespeare's characters and scenarios have proved an enduring inspiration for composers across the centuries

The man that hath no music in himself,
Nor is not moved with concord of
   sweet sounds,
Is fit for treasons, stratagems and spoils [...]
Let no such man be trusted.

We cannot say for certain that these words, spoken by Lorenzo in *The Merchant of Venice*, reflect its author's own opinions but Shakespeare undoubtedly knew a lot about music and cared greatly for it. His plays are full of cues for fanfares and marches, dances and serenades; music heightens emotional situations such as the suffering of Richard II in his prison cell and the reunion of King Lear with his daughter Cordelia; it is often associated with the supernatural, as with the Witches in *Macbeth* and the spirit Ariel in *The Tempest* (perhaps the most musical of all the plays); it accompanies the apparent resurrection of Thaisa in *Pericles* and of Hermione in *The Winter's Tale*; Ophelia in her madness sings snatches of old songs; in *Othello* Desdemona's singing of the Willow Song provides a poignant moment of repose before

her murder. Shakespeare writes tender songs for Feste in *Twelfth Night* and for Lear's Fool, both with the singing actor Robert Armin originally in mind. Even the monster Caliban, in *The Tempest*, knows that Prospero's island is 'full of sounds and sweet airs that give delight, and hurt not'. In *Twelfth Night* and in *The Tempest*, raucous music underpins drunken revels, and dislike of music is a symptom of malignancy in Shylock and Iago.

Lorenzo speaks in blank verse, the standard form for Shakespearean drama, made up of 10-syllabled iambic pentameter lines, 'blank' in the sense that it is generally unrhymed, though rhyme may be used too. But Shakespeare never uses blank verse for words that he intends to be sung, which are always set off from the surrounding dialogue by being written in lyric measures, often marked by repetitions and refrains, and with a relatively low density of meaning.

Shakespeare knew that verse meant to be set to music benefits from simplicity of expression

and can accommodate repetitions – as in these words sung by the page boys in *As You Like It*:

It was a lover and his lass,
With a hey, and a ho, and a hey-nonny-no,
That o'er the green cornfields did pass
In spring-time, the only pretty ring-time,
When birds do sing, hey ding-a-ding ding,
Sweet lovers love the spring.

This helps to explain why few of the great musical settings of Shakespeare's words draw on the dialogue of the plays. There are exceptions, such as Vaughan Williams's ravishing *Serenade to Music*, which sets Lorenzo's speech from *The Merchant of Venice* quoted at the start of this article, but there the music is lyrically rhapsodic rather than dramatic, reflecting the 'soft harmonies' of the verse, and casting the words into second place. Among the few outstanding English operas based on Shakespeare, Benjamin Britten's *A Midsummer Night's Dream* is unusual in making few changes other than cuts to the original dialogue; whereas Thomas Adès's *The Tempest* has a libretto that strips

Shakespeare's words to the bone, turning even long speeches into brief verses resembling the lyrics of his plays.

Sadly, although some of the greatest composers of Shakespeare's time, such as Thomas Morley, Robert Johnson and John Dowland, wrote for

> " Sadly, although some of the greatest composers of Shakespeare's time wrote for the theatre, very little original music for his plays survives. "

the theatre, very little original music for his plays survives. On the plus side, however, this has stimulated many composers of later periods – as various as Mendelssohn, Arthur Sullivan, Erich Korngold, William Walton and Patrick Doyle – to write new music for the stage and, in more recent times, for films. Changing staging methods call for new styles of music, so that for example Mendelssohn writes a wedding march for *A Midsummer Night's Dream* lasting some seven minutes for an episode which in Shakespeare's theatre would have been far shorter.

Shakespearean drama – with its high passions, its soliloquies and mad scenes, its dances and battles and formalised conversations, its love scenes and lyrical interludes, and even its comic set pieces – has much in common with opera and indeed has exerted a profound influence upon operatic conventions. Ophelia's musical mad scene is surely the origin of many *bravura*

set pieces in the operas of composers such as Bellini, Donizetti and Ambroise Thomas, and even of the mad episode in Britten's *Peter Grimes*. Mozart is said to have been contemplating an opera based on *The Tempest* late in his life – what a loss was there! Rossini's *Otello*, with three virtuoso tenor roles and a lovely setting of Desdemona's Willow Song, would be better known than it is had it not been eclipsed by Verdi's late masterpiece. Verdi had already written a *Macbeth*, with a wonderfully eerie setting of the sleepwalking scene. His final opera, *Falstaff*, based mainly on *The Merry Wives of Windsor* but also incorporating Falstaff's great 'honour' soliloquy from *Henry IV, Part 1*, has similarly overshadowed Otto Nicolai's charming *The Merry Wives of Windsor*, known, at least in the UK, mainly by its overture. Verdi and Britten contemplated writing operas based on *King Lear* but didn't get round to this daunting task. Debussy began sketching some incidental music for the play, but he too soon gave up.

Hector Berlioz was one of Shakespeare's most passionate admirers. He fell in love simultaneously with Shakespeare and the actress Harriet Smithson, whom he later married, when he saw performances given by a company performing in English (which he didn't understand) in Paris in 1827. One result was a string of great if eccentric compositions, including a concert overture to *King Lear*; a funeral march for *Hamlet* which calls for a large orchestra along with a wordless chorus; an opera, *Beatrice and Benedict*, based on *Much Ado About Nothing*, whose overture dazzlingly encapsulates the lovers' battles of wit; and, greatest of all, the dramatic symphony *Romeo and Juliet*, at the heart of which lies the wordless but pulsatingly beautiful

Love Scene. Typically, Berlioz picks out plums from the story without attempting to reflect the play's structure. Tchaikovsky's much-loved fantasy-overture inspired by the same play, however, follows the drama's main sequence of events from the clashing swords of the opening bars through the romance of the lovers' meeting to the subdued pathos of their deaths. Somewhat similarly, Edward Elgar's symphonic study *Falstaff* movingly follows the character's fortunes through the *Henry IV* plays to the report of his death in *Henry V*, with two retrospective orchestral interludes recalling Falstaff's earlier days. ›

Ophelia, whose dramatic mad scene in *Hamlet* gave rise to what has become a set-piece challenge to opera composers (painting, 1910, by John William Waterhouse)

IMAGINATION BEYOND WORDS

Hilary Finch discovers how some of the composers of Shakespeare-inspired works at this year's Proms have conjured myriad sounds around the Bard's texts

'Feed him with apricots and dewberries': Titania instructs her fairies to attend Bottom in Act 3 Scene 1 of *A Midsummer Night's Dream* (painting by John Anster Fitzgerald, c1820–1906)

To begin at the end … Shakespeare's last plays – *Cymbeline*, *The Winter's Tale* and *The Tempest* – share with music a quest for a transcendent reality beyond words. As such, they have proved highly seductive, but also formidably challenging, for composers. *The Tempest*, with its landscape of 'sounds and sweet airs', has proved by far the most irresistible to composers from Locke and Berlioz to Frank Martin, Michael Nyman, Thomas Adès and Judith Weir, and perhaps not least to Sibelius. A commission for incidental music came from Copenhagen's Royal Theatre in 1925, immediately preceding Sibelius's 30-year creative silence. As such, it is impossible not to ponder on the composer's own preoccupations at this stage in his career – and to speculate on the kinship he felt with Prospero who, at the end of *The Tempest*, abjures the 'rough magic' of his own art. Sibelius's overture to *The Tempest* reveals both ripeness and the deeply felt potential for chaos within the composer's own 'so potent art', in its sea-surge of strings, its livid gleams of woodwind and its howling horns.

Prospero's great valedictory speech proved just the thing with which to celebrate the ending of the revels of Italy's Batignano Festival in 2004. Jonathan Dove's eight-minute recessional, a setting for baritone, vocal ensemble and orchestra of 'Our revels now are ended', is very much an occasional piece – but one which is clearly the work of a composer intensely engaged with the theatre: Dove has written incidental music for both *All's Well That Ends Well* and *A Midsummer Night's Dream*. So far, though, Dove has yet to write a Shakespearean opera.

Songs without words were very much Mendelssohn's thing. And, although he did set one of Shakespeare's songs within his incidental music for *A Midsummer Night's Dream*, his most evocative music is for orchestra alone. So-called 'melodramas' – in which music heightens the effect of spoken text – are threaded through a score whose overture represents a fragrant flowering of the responses of an introspective 17-year-old. On first reading Shakespeare's play, the young Mendelssohn wrote to his sister Fanny of his 'fantastic, dream-like life'.

No wonder, then, that a composer of such delicate imaginings, wit and refinement should have been deeply shocked, at their meeting in Rome in 1831, at the more intemperate responses to Shakespeare of Hector Berlioz.

No composer's life was so thoroughly, consistently and feverishly dominated by the playwright's inspiration. Berlioz was 24 when his first encounter with Shakespeare, at the hands of an English troupe visiting Paris, enflamed his emotions. Never before had he experienced such 'true grandeur, true beauty, dramatic truth'. And never before had he seen the actress Harriet Smithson. His infatuation for her was inextricably fused with his passion for Shakespeare. After their ruinous marriage and Smithson's death, Berlioz exclaimed, 'Shakespeare! Shakespeare! Where is he? He alone among intelligent beings can understand me, and must have understood us both!' Cue for *Romeo and Juliet*, the extended and unique dramatic symphony which reveals Berlioz's all-consuming identification with Romeo: 'That is me, yes me!' he shamelessly declared. The 'Queen Mab' Scherzo (an idea suggested by Mendelssohn) is, like Berlioz's *Much Ado* opera *Beatrice and Benedict*, a 'caprice written with the point of a needle'. As an early commentator wrote of the opera, 'Gay, caustic, occasionally poetic, it brings a smile to the eye and to the lips.'

Tchaikovsky's fantasy-overture *Romeo and Juliet* is perhaps his most popular; but, following his symphonic fantasy *The Tempest*, the fantasy-overture *Hamlet* is arguably the most striking of the composer's engagements with Shakespeare. Commentators frequently try, somewhat

strenuously, to detect a narrative within the work's 18 or so minutes. But this piece, significantly a contemporary of the Fifth Symphony, is primarily an evocation of the composer's personal empathy for Shakespeare's Hamlet: his self-doubt, his conflicted soul, his sense of the inescapable pursuit of Fate.

Ophelia's spirit, perhaps, hovers over Tchaikovsky's score in the plangent voice of the oboe. Hans Abrahamsen's Ophelian *let me tell you*, a song-cycle for soprano and orchestra premiered in 2013, led one critic to declare that he 'felt inside a snow globe, watching flakes fall in exquisite slow motion'. And, in Paul Griffiths's text, it is indeed snow, rather than the waters of a stream, that sends this Ophelia into oblivion. Abrahamsen here seems as much inspired by Griffiths's text – based on a 2008 novel in which he had fashioned a first-person narrative entirely from the 481 words given to Ophelia in the original play – as he is by Shakespeare himself. Both writer and composer are bewitched by repetition, transformation, metamorphosis – and it is this potent meeting of two minds that creates for our own decade and century a reinvention of Shakespeare that is truly rich and strange.

Hilary Finch was for 35 years a music critic for The Times and she broadcasts regularly on BBC Radio 3. As a freelance writer she specialises in the field of song, and in the music and literature of the Nordic countries.

ROYAL SHAKESPEARE COMPANY

1616–2016
MAKE THIS THE YEAR
TO CELEBRATE SHAKESPEARE

AUGUST 2016–FEBRUARY 2017

A MIDSUMMER NIGHT'S DREAM
WILLIAM SHAKESPEARE

HAMLET
WILLIAM SHAKESPEARE

KING LEAR
WILLIAM SHAKESPEARE

CYMBELINE
WILLIAM SHAKESPEARE

THE ROYAL SHAKESPEARE COMPANY IN COLLABORATION WITH INTEL
THE TEMPEST
WILLIAM SHAKESPEARE

DOCTOR FAUSTUS
CHRISTOPHER MARLOWE

DON QUIXOTE
ADAPTED BY JAMES FENTON FROM THE NOVEL BY MIGUEL DE CERVANTES

THE ALCHEMIST
BEN JONSON

THE TWO NOBLE KINSMEN
JOHN FLETCHER & WILLIAM SHAKESPEARE

THE ROVER
APHRA BEHN

THE SEVEN ACTS OF MERCY
ANDERS LUSTGARTEN

ARTS COUNCIL ENGLAND

Supported using public funding by
ARTS COUNCIL ENGLAND

Shakespeare adopted many of the conventions of the popular theatre of his time – comic routines, song interludes, dance episodes – and these are often reflected in musicals based on his plays. One of the most successful of all adaptations of *Romeo and Juliet* is Leonard Bernstein's jazz-inspired *West Side Story*, with its exhilarating dances; and Cole Porter's *Kiss Me, Kate*, based on *The Taming of the Shrew*, has as its hit number the catchy 'Brush up your Shakespeare, / Start quoting him now', with its witty puns on the titles of the plays. There is even a rock *Othello*.

Jazz composers have responded to Shakespeare too. *Sweet Thunder*, a sequence of music by Duke Ellington and Billy Strayhorn commissioned by the Stratford (Ontario) Festival in 1956, sets lyrics associated in various ways with the dramatist, and in 1963 Ellington composed incidental music for the Festival's production of the rarely performed *Timon of Athens*. John Dankworth is another jazz composer who has set Shakespeare; the 2007 Prom entitled 'From Bards to Blues' featured Shakespeare settings by both Dankworth and Ellington.

To paraphrase Falstaff, Shakespeare was not only musical in himself, but over the centuries has also been the cause that vast quantities of great music have come into being, inspired by the structure of his plays, the passions of their characters, their lyrical beauty and their emotional power. ●

Author and scholar Stanley Wells is Emeritus Professor of Shakespeare Studies at the University of Birmingham, co-editor of the Oxford *Complete Works* and general editor of the Oxford Shakespeare series. He is also Honorary President of the Shakespeare Birthplace Trust, Honorary Governor Emeritus of the Royal Shakespeare Company and a member of the Board of Directors of the Globe Theatre. He was appointed CBE in 2007.

Leonard Whiting as Romeo and Olivia Hussey as Juliet in Franco Zeffirelli's 1968 film adaptation of *Romeo and Juliet*

....

Tchaikovsky Fantasy-Overture 'Romeo and Juliet'
PROM 1 • 15 JULY

Fauré Shylock
PROM 7 • 20 JULY

Tchaikovsky The Tempest
PROM 15 • 26 JULY

Prokofiev Romeo and Juliet – excerpts
PROM 16 • 27 JULY

Berlioz Beatrice and Benedict – overture
PROM 17 • 28 JULY

Berlioz Romeo and Juliet
PROM 20 • 30 JULY

Debussy, orch. Roger-Ducasse King Lear – Fanfare d'ouverture; Le sommeil de Lear
PROM 22 • 31 JULY

Sibelius The Tempest – Prelude
PROM 23 • 1 AUGUST

Duke Ellington Such Sweet Thunder
PROM 28 • 5 AUGUST

Music for and inspired by *Timon of Athens*, *The Tempest*, *A Midsummer Night's Dream* (Purcell, Locke, *etc.*)
PROMS AT ... SAM WANAMAKER PLAYHOUSE • 13 AUGUST

Berlioz Overture 'King Lear'
PROM 41 • 16 AUGUST

Shakespeare: Stage and Screen
PROM 44 • 18 AUGUST

Shakespeare choral settings by Johnson, Morley, Nico Muhly and Huw Watkins
PROMS CHAMBER MUSIC 5 15 AUGUST

Mendelssohn A Midsummer Night's Dream – overture and incidental music
PROM 48 • 21 AUGUST

Tchaikovsky Fantasy-Overture 'Hamlet'
PROM 50 • 23 AUGUST

Hans Abrahamsen let me tell you
PROM 55 • 27 AUGUST

Shakespeare settings by Purcell (arr. Britten) and Quilter
PROMS CHAMBER MUSIC 8 5 SEPTEMBER

Vaughan Williams Serenade to Music; **Jonathan Dove** Our revels now are ended
PROM 75 • 10 SEPTEMBER

THEATRE IN THE BLOOD

From the cunning Barber of Seville to the scheming Queen of Babylon, two Rossini operas – and the curious, paradoxical *Petite messe solennelle* – present Rossini at his dramatic best. **Alexandra Wilson** discovers how

Gioachino Rossini was the undisputed operatic king of the early 19th century. Between 1810 and 1829 he turned out opera after opera with apparent ease, writing some, including *The Barber of Seville*, in a matter of weeks. His works were famous across Europe and composers for generations to come would feel obliged to confront 'the Rossini legacy'. But then, after the triumph of *William Tell* in Paris in 1829, he abruptly abandoned operatic composition in early middle age for reasons that remain unclear: perhaps because of ill health, perhaps because he had amassed enough money to last a lifetime, or perhaps because he was simply exhausted after writing 39 operas in under 20 years. He was to live for almost four more decades.

The two operas being performed in this Proms season, *The Barber of Seville* (1816) and *Semiramide* (1823), represent two contrasting musical 'faces' of Rossini – the comic and the serious – but both were composed during the same phase of his career, his 'Italian' period. The *Petite messe solennelle* (1864), on the other hand, was written several decades later, by which time the musical world had changed enormously: Wagner's *Tristan and Isolde*, for example, would receive its premiere the following year. Meanwhile Verdi had long since jettisoned the operatic conventions he had inherited from Rossini.

Rossini was a man of apparent contradictions: by turns witty yet melancholic, conservative yet groundbreaking, a hyper-productive figure on the international musical stage who then fell apparently idle for decades (though behind the scenes he continued to write numerous salon pieces). There are also pointed contrasts in the contexts that shaped the three main works we hear this season. *The Barber of Seville* was composed during a period of stability in Rossini's career. He had been hired by the impresario Domenico Barbaia to work at the Teatro San Carlo in Naples, a post that gave him financial stability and creative freedom. Although the emphasis at the San Carlo was on *opera seria* (based on heroic or tragic subjects), Rossini's contract allowed him the flexibility to write operas for other cities: *The Barber of Seville* was premiered in Rome.

By contrast *Semiramide*, first performed at the Teatro La Fenice in Venice, was written at a time of flux and was to be Rossini's last opera for Italy. Nervous about political unrest and in need of fresh artistic challenges, he was

> ❝
> Rossini was a man of apparent contradictions: by turns witty yet melancholic, conservative yet groundbreaking, a hyper-productive figure who then fell apparently idle for decades. ❞

keen to move on from Naples. The *Petite messe solennelle*, meanwhile, appeared at an even more difficult time in Rossini's life, arising from a final burst of creative energy at a time when he was worn out by numerous health problems.

Rossini covered a wide range of subjects in his operas. Like Verdi, he was drawn to the works

of Shakespeare and Schiller (he wrote operas on *Othello* and *William Tell*), while also drawing inspiration from contemporary Romantic poetry (*La donna del lago* – 'The Lady of the Lake' – after Walter Scott) and even fairy tale (*La Cenerentola*, 'Cinderella'). His tastes, then, were cosmopolitan, but he was particularly fascinated by French subjects, even before establishing his 'second career' in Paris. Despite being written for Italian theatres and exhibiting many characteristic Italian musical conventions, *The Barber of Seville* and *Semiramide* were both based upon classic French 18th-century literary texts.

Pierre Beaumarchais's *Le barbier de Séville* (1775) was the first part of a trilogy of comic plays that epitomised Enlightenment values in their undermining of social hierarchies. The play lent itself well to operatic treatment (indeed, Beaumarchais originally envisaged it as an *opéra comique*) and in 1782 it was set as an *opera buffa* by Giovanni Paisiello. (Mozart's setting of the second work in the trilogy – *Le mariage de Figaro* – would follow four years later.) Paisiello's work was well-loved by the time Rossini came along but the younger composer would trump his success with an opera of greater wit, irony and melodic invention.

The characters and situations in Beaumarchais's play mapped well onto the stock conventions of *opera buffa*, such as disguise, *imbroglio* (comic confusion) and buffoonery. *The Barber*'s storyline, about how an old man's plan to marry his young ward is thwarted by a young admirer who conspires with a cunning servant, was a familiar Italian plot-type with roots in the *commedia dell'arte* tradition. Figaro, the roguish barber of the title, is himself a

Rossini, c1860, a few years before writing his *Petite messe solennelle*: though long into retirement, he had by now begun composing the salon pieces he fondly described as his 'Sins of Old Age'

Harlequin-like figure, who weaves dramatic intrigue and steps outside the action to address the audience directly in his famous patter aria 'Largo al factotum'.

Whereas *The Barber* deals with 'real' characters whose foibles are exposed to comic effect, in *Semiramide* there is a sense of remove between the audience and the action on stage. Following the typical *opera seria* conventions, the characters inhabit an elevated social milieu, a distant past and a remote location (ancient Babylon). Like *The Barber*, *Semiramide* centres around a love triangle and elements of mistaken identity, but there

THE HARMONIUM

The gently bleating organ-like instrument which Rossini featured in his Petite messe solennelle

The painter Cristiano Banti at the harmonium, by Giovanni Boldini (1842–1931)

The harmonium, a small member of the reed organ family, was a relatively new invention at the time Rossini employed it in his *Petite messe solennelle* of 1864. The instrument had been patented only in the early 1840s by the Parisian inventor Alexandre-François Debain. The harmonium player uses two pedals operated by the feet to drive air through bellows. Over time Debain tinkered with his design, improving what was initially an expressively rather limited instrument by finding a way of enabling it to produce fluctuations of volume. Relying on reeds rather than pipes, it could serve a variety of practical applications: it could be used in churches where space was limited and it even became a popular instrument in middle-class 19th-century homes. Nevertheless, keen to exploit the harmonium's particular sound – combining the tone qualities of an organ and an accordion – many composers used it in large-scale works. Richard Strauss employed one in his opera *Ariadne auf Naxos*, as did Mahler in his Eighth Symphony. Schoenberg, meanwhile, arranged a number of orchestral works by Mahler, Bruckner and Debussy for harmonium, piano and a small string-and-wind ensemble. Harmoniums were exported to India in the 19th century and took on an important role in Indian music.

the dramatic similarities end: the plot deals with incestuous desire, political ambition, matricide and supernatural intervention. Yet, despite this apparent remoteness, the opera contains a complex, tragic heroine who experiences the full range of human emotions and displays great psychological depth. Rossini created the role for his wife, Isabella Colbran, and the vocal writing is among the most florid and demanding he would write in any opera.

The *Petite messe solennelle* seems in some ways to have appeared out of nowhere. But, like most Italian opera composers, Rossini had dabbled periodically in sacred music, writing a *Messa di Gloria* (1820), a *Stabat mater* (1832) and numerous small-scale religious works across his career. With the *Petite messe*, however, we have the sense that Rossini was consciously writing a swansong: his preface to the piece, addressed to God, concludes: 'Be blessed, then, and admit me to Paradise.' The work is hardly 'petite' in its proportions, although it is certainly pared-down in its unusual original scoring for choir, two pianos and harmonium (the composer would later rescore it for choir and orchestra).

Rossini envisaged the work for 12 voices (representing the Apostles), in stark contrast to the immense vocal forces required for many 19th-century Masses, such as Berlioz's *Grande messe des morts* (*Requiem*). The small forces reflected the fact that the piece was first performed in an intimate setting, for the dedication of a private chapel in Paris belonging to some of Rossini's aristocratic friends. In the preface to the score, Rossini jokes about whether the piece is sacred music at all: certainly there are distant echoes of his

earlier operatic writing, but overall the style is eclectic, some movements looking back to Palestrina, others seeming to pre-empt the sacred music of the early 20th century. In message too, the work is enigmatic: some movements are pervaded by an almost eerie sense of anxiety, while others are radiantly joyful.

The musical canon is a fickle beast and, despite Rossini's immense popularity during his operatic career, many of his works had already

Available for shaves and serenades: the resourceful factotum Figaro (portrait of baritone Giorgio Ronconi, 1810–90) in the title-role of Rossini's *The Barber of Seville*

fallen out of favour before his own death. A gradual Rossini renaissance began in the 1920s and gathered pace as the 20th century progressed. Composers also began to rediscover him: Benjamin Britten, for example, arranged a series of frothy Rossini salon pieces in the lushly orchestrated suites *Soirées musicales* (first performed in 1937) and *Matinées musicales* (1941), both of which were choreographed as ballets by George Balanchine, and both of which can be heard at this year's Last Night.

The Barber of Seville, though, is unusual in being the opera that never really went away. Despite an inauspicious start – a claque

Voltaire reading his tragedy *Sémiramis* to King Stanisław of Poland (illustration for *The World's Great Books*, 1910): the play inspired *Semiramide*, Rossini's last opera for Italy before his move to Paris

Like *The Barber of Seville*, *Semiramide* centres around a love triangle and elements of mistaken identity, but there the dramatic similarities end.

believed to have been Paisiello supporters disturbed the first night – it is the earliest Rossini opera to have remained continuously within the repertoire. Similarly, *Semiramide* can make a claim to have been Rossini's most enduring serious opera. It was an immediate success at its premiere and, although it came to be regarded as stylistically old-fashioned within a comparatively short time, continued to be performed throughout the 19th century. The reason is a simple one: its dramatically rewarding title-role and show-stopping arias such as 'Bel raggio lusinghier' led *prime*

donne such as Adelina Patti and Nellie Melba to keep it alive. The work lost some status in the early 20th century but enjoyed a revival on stage and on record from the 1960s, partly because it was a favourite of Joan Sutherland's.

Reflecting back on his career in the preface to the *Petite messe solennelle*, Rossini wrote, 'I was born for comic opera.' His reputation in the field of comedy is certainly justified – Verdi called *The Barber of Seville* 'the finest *opera buffa* in existence' – but, as the other two Rossini works in this Proms season demonstrate, together with the homage to him by Britten, there is much more to the composer than this. ●

Alexandra Wilson is Reader in Musicology at Oxford Brookes University, where she co-directs the OBERTO opera research unit and teaches courses on opera. She is the author of *The Puccini Problem: Opera, Nationalism, and Modernity* and *Opera: A Beginner's Guide*.

The Barber of Seville

PROM 14 • 25 JULY

Petite messe solennelle

PROMS AT … THE CHAPEL, OLD ROYAL NAVAL COLLEGE, GREENWICH • 6 AUGUST

Soirées musicales (arr. Liszt) – La regata veneziana (notturno); La danza (tarantella)

PROMS CHAMBER MUSIC 6 22 AUGUST

Semiramide

PROM 68 • 4 SEPTEMBER

Matinées musicales (arr. Britten)

PROM 75 • 10 SEPTEMBER

Shakespeare's
New Place
Opening July 2016

Stratford-upon-Avon's newest and most exciting attraction

- Visit the most significant heritage site celebrating 400 years of Shakespeare's legacy

- Walk in Shakespeare's footsteps and trace the footprint of his family home

- Meet the man behind the works in a fascinating new exhibition

- Discover beautiful gardens and specially-commissioned artworks

To find out more about this world-class project visit: shakespeare.org.uk

Shakespeare birthplace trust

shakespeare.org.uk

New Place
The site of Shakespeare's family home from 1597 to 1616

'And to thee and thy company I bid
A hearty welcome'   The Tempest, Act 5 Scene 1

 Supported by
Historic England

 heritage lottery fund
LOTTERY FUNDED

His **footsteps,**
your **journey**

Registered Charity Number 209302

Celebrate William Shakespeare

Contemporary coins for a man way ahead of his time

William Shakespeare is one of the greatest writers who ever lived, whose plays and words are still as stirring and relevant today as in Shakespeare's own time. In 2016, in the year of the 400th anniversary of his death, The Royal Mint is proud to strike a range of coins celebrating the playwright and his great works.

Experienced coinage artist John Bergdahl has created bold designs, which capture the passion of Shakespeare's work. Three coins represent Shakespeare's most famous bodies of work, his comedies, histories and tragedies.

The Shakespeare 2016 UK £2 Silver Proof Coins

- Three individual coins represent Shakespeare's comedies, histories and tragedies
- Struck in 925 sterling silver, finished to Proof standard
- Just 5,000 Limited Edition Issue of each coin are available
- Endorsed by the Shakespeare Birthplace Trust

PRICE: £60.00*

Treasure *for* Life™

 Online: royalmint.com/shakespeare
(For FREE UK delivery on orders over £45 please enter the Promotional Code P1619B on Your Basket page)

 Phone: 0845 450 38 06
(Lines open 9am-6pm Monday-Sunday)

 /theroyalmint   @RoyalMintUK

P1619B

HOME OF **THE CODEBREAKERS**

Once Britain's Best Kept Secret, today Bletchley Park is a heritage site and vibrant tourist attraction. Open daily, visitors can explore the iconic WW2 Codebreaking Huts and Blocks and marvel at the astonishing achievements of the Codebreakers whose work helped shorten the war.

For directions and more details visit **www.bletchleypark.org.uk**

BLETCHLEYPARK

Cello by
Matthew Hardie
Edinburgh c.1800

F.N. Voirin, Paris, c.1875-78

Cello by
Joseph Hill, London
c.1770-1780

Eugene Sartory
Paris, c.1930

Tom Woods
LONDON'S CELLO SPECIALIST
www.tomwoodscellos.com
+44 (0)20 7362 1812

Nicolas Leonard Tourte
Paris, c.1785-80

Cello by
Albert Caressa
Paris, c.1926

Victor Fetique, Paris, c.1925

Cello by
Louis Guersan
Paris, c.1760

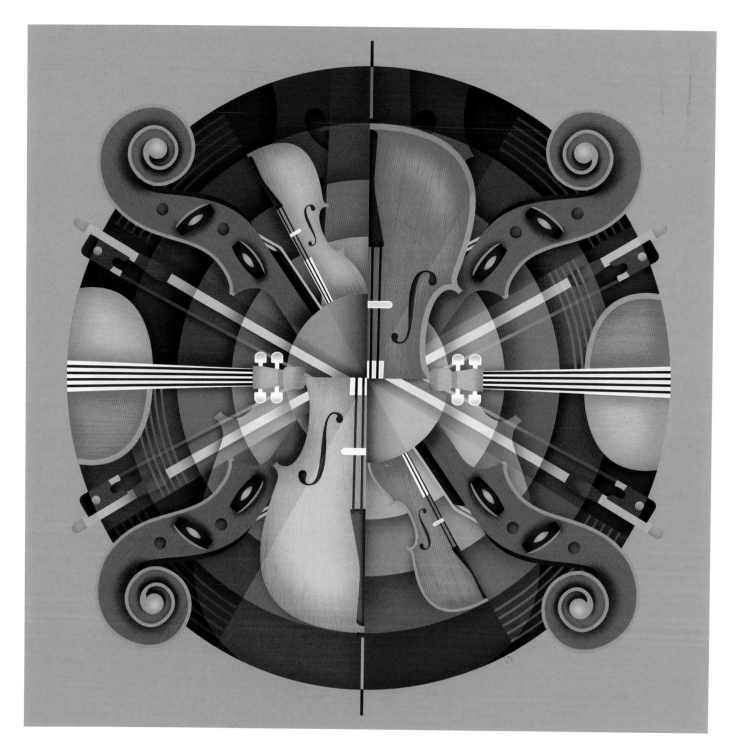

NO MORE SECOND FIDDLE

With no fewer than 10 cello concertos at the Proms this year, plus a Proms Chamber Music concert featuring multiple cellos, **Mats Lidström** makes the case for an instrument often overshadowed by its better-known musical cousins

The beautiful truth about the cello is that it enjoys a special place in people's hearts. Of all the instruments, the cello is the one which most often provokes a sigh of contentment and a smile of recognition in the listener. Time and again one finds this reaction. The strongest 'rivals' in terms of popularity are the piano, violin and voice. These may have a wider repertoire compared with the cello, but I believe there is an immediacy to the warmly resonant and dark-toned richness of the cello – a uniquely profound and human depth – that reaches directly to the soul. The cello seems to communicate tenderness and warmth like nothing else, and it can seem like a magical, natural bridge between the music and the listener.

It's sometimes easy to forget the cello's wide range of pitch, which spans not only the lower, 'male' range, but also – equally well exploited for expressive effect – the upper, 'female' range – a feature that already leaves behind the voice and violin. The recurring comment from listeners, though, is that they particularly love the 'baritone' or middle register of the cello, an especially 'sweet' spot in its range. Think of Saint-Saëns's cello solo 'The Swan' from *The Carnival of the Animals* – lyrical, graceful and serene. This piece reached a whole new audience through Anna Pavlova's solo ballet *The Dying Swan*, created for her in 1905 by Mikhail Fokine (who later choreographed Stravinsky's *The Firebird* and *Petrushka*). The visual drama of the choreography – billowing arms above the waist contrasting with quivering little steps below – is a breathtakingly poignant complement to the music. Pavlova performed it more than 4,000 times all over the world, contributing to the legendary status of this cello solo. A cornerstone of our repertoire, 'The Swan' glides in parallel with all else in a cellist's life.

'Monsieur, you make me believe in miracles. You know how to make a nightingale out of an ox!' This was the writer Voltaire's comment after hearing French cellist Jean-Louis Duport (1749–1819), one of the great cellists of the 18th century. Beethoven loved Duport's playing, too, and wrote his first two

Russian ballerina Svetlana Zakharova in Mikhail Fokine's *The Dying Swan*, featuring Saint-Saëns's 'The Swan', at the Gala des Étoiles, Luxembourg, 2015

WRITING FOR THE CELLO

Huw Watkins, whose new Cello Concerto is performed by his brother Paul (Prom 37), recalls growing up with the instrument and its repertoire

My brother Paul is six years older than me, so there was always much catching up for me to do during our childhood. Paul encouraged me to practise by showing me repertoire that was a little too hard: first, sonatas by Bach and Beethoven; and, later on, more exotic 20th-century works. (Elliott Carter's sonata made a huge impression when I was about 12.) In this way, I got to play through an enormous amount of music for cello and piano, all the time trying to remember what worked well and what didn't. At the same time, I was writing cello-and-piano pieces which we would try out. Throughout the process of writing my first cello concerto, I have kept thinking how closely connected the cello and my brother are in my mind, making it impossible to write for the instrument without imagining his wonderfully expressive sound. Another of his many qualities is that of bringing the same type of commitment and passion to a new or obscure piece as he would to an old warhorse. For me, that means there is little temptation to indulge in any modish extended playing techniques, instead trusting that he will communicate a musical line with great clarity and expression.

The cello music that Rostropovich brought to life must in some way have influenced every composer writing for the cello since then – it certainly has for me. Three concertos as different as Shostakovich's, Britten's and Lutosławski's suggest ways of doing things that, for example, Haydn and Schumann don't; and it's easy to imagine those pieces not existing at all, were it not for Rostropovich's persuasiveness.

Cello Sonatas for him. Voltaire's comment illustrates the popular attitude towards the cello and how desperately behind the violin it was at this time in terms of solo status. Among the French, especially, the cello was seen as a clumsy rival to their beloved viola da gamba (literally, 'leg viol'), an attitude which prevailed all the way into the 1780s.

The Catalan cellist Pablo Casals (1876–1973) has been credited with bringing the cello closer to the piano and the violin in terms of establishing it as a solo instrument. He invented the stretching technique of the left-hand fingers, increasing their independence, in order to make the fingerboard appear 'smaller'. Prior to this practice, the constant shifting between positions on the fingerboard created a series of swooping shifts, or mini glissandos, as the fingers glided between positions. This effect had been one of the reasons behind George Bernard Shaw's dislike of the cello. He lived across the courtyard from the famous cellist Joseph Hollman (1852–1926), dedicatee of Saint-Saëns's Cello Concerto No. 2 and Massenet's Cello Concerto, and would hold his hands over his ears when Hollman practised. However, Shaw later heard Casals play and was able to change his mind. The great cellist David Popper (1843–1913), whose 40 great studies are still a staple of the cello student's training after more than 100 years, once heard his younger colleague Casals play a recital. He realised cello-playing had entered a new era, a move away from the ideals of the 19th century.

The swiftness in Casals's playing was nothing new, but the focus on sound and articulation (attack) were. This can be heard in a 1915 recording by Casals of Popper's Mazurka, Op. 11 No. 3. Compared to other recordings from this time, and even later, Casals presents a sheer power of volume which had not been experienced before. But it would be a mistake to say that there were no virtuosos before him. One need only look at the pieces that were available to cellists. There were several composers already in the 18th century, besides Haydn and Boccherini, who wrote technically highly demanding works. Then, with the arrival in the early 19th century of virtuosos such as Paganini and Liszt, a flood of showpieces for the cello also appeared, attracting virtuosos from across Europe. Bernhard Romberg (1767–1841) was famous for his ample sound, but this aspect of cello-playing was increasingly ignored as more attention was given to the left hand: the new priority was to dazzle the audience with bravura numbers similar to those of Paganini. The case of Romberg is a slightly sensitive one. As Europe's leading cellist, he was approached by Beethoven, who wanted to write a concerto for him. Romberg apparently answered that he only played his own concertos: there are

David Popper (1843–1913), the cellist whose 40 studies remain a mainstay in training today's cello students

Benjamin Ealovega (Watkins), Lebrecht Music & Arts (Popper)

10 of them, plus six concertinos, so that would have been enough to keep him busy. In any case, Beethoven abandoned his own plan. Any sketch for a cello concerto found its way into the Triple Concerto – for violin, cello and piano with orchestra – where the cello part is featured unusually prominently. Whenever I play any works by Romberg, I cannot help asking myself if he was responsible for the fact that Beethoven never wrote a cello concerto.

The cello repertoire is large and diverse. Yet, of the 200 or so cello concertos written in the 19th century, we regularly play only four today: Schumann, Tchaikovsky, Saint-Saëns's No. 1 and Dvořák. A number of concertos by now-neglected composers, such as Bernhard Molique, Robert Volkmann, Léon Boëllmann and Eugen d'Albert, were previously standard repertoire, played by every cellist on the solo circuit. Today those pieces are forgotten, but on the other hand new ones continue to appear. We cellists need to look into this historical treasure trove, though, to avoid over-exposing the same pieces. There are always alternatives to any standard repertoire work and some of them are truly masterful. It is tremendously rewarding to uncover and restore these works. It is also a wonderful way for the cellist to create a personal solo repertoire, and an eye-opening reminder that composers, representing all sorts of styles, have for hundreds of years chosen to write music for the cello. The three new concertos at this year's Proms – by Thomas Adès, Charlotte Bray and Huw Watkins – show that there is a strong future for the cello concerto, too. ●

Mats Lidström is a cellist, composer, arranger and a professor of cello at the Royal Academy of Music, London. In addition to the standard repertoire, he has championed cello concertos by Kabalevsky, Khachaturian, Korngold and Rolf Martinsson, among others.

Pablo Casals (1876–1973), one of the 20th century's most celebrated cellists, who developed the technique of stretching the left-hand fingers across the fingerboard in order to avoid sliding between positions

....

Elgar Cello Concerto
Sol Gabetta *cello*
PROM 1 • 15 JULY

Debussy Cello Sonata
Bjørg Lewis *cello*
PROMS CHAMBER MUSIC 1 • 18 JULY

Guy Johnston and friends *cellos*
PROMS CHAMBER MUSIC 2 • 25 JULY

Dvořák Cello Concerto
Alban Gerhardt *cello*
PROM 25 • 3 AUGUST

Dutilleux
'Tout un monde lointain …'
Johannes Moser *cello*
PROM 33 • 9 AUGUST

Huw Watkins Cello Concerto
BBC commission: world premiere
Paul Watkins *cello*
PROM 37 • 12 AUGUST

Charlotte Bray Falling in the Fire
BBC commission: world premiere
Guy Johnston *cello*
PROM 39 • 14 AUGUST

Thomas Adès Lieux retrouvés
world premiere of version
with orchestra
Steven Isserlis *cello*
PROMS 40 • 15 AUGUST

Colin Matthews
Berceuse for Dresden
London premiere
Leonard Elschenbroich *cello*
PROM 41 • 16 AUGUST

Haydn Cello Concerto No. 1
Narek Hakhnazaryan *cello*
PROM 47 • 21 AUGUST

Shostakovich Cello Concerto No. 1
Truls Mørk *cello*
PROM 53 • 25 AUGUST

LOVE
MUSIC
HELP
MUSICIANS UK

I'm a violinist and
Help Musicians UK helped me
financially and emotionally
when I had cancer.

Your support means we can
help more people like Mandhira.
Help us help musicians.

Donate at helpmusicians.org.uk
or call 020 7239 9100

Backing musicians throughout their careers.
Registered charity No. 228089.

MY PROMS

CERYS MATTHEWS

singer, broadcaster

I've been a Proms-goer for as long as I can remember. I played oboe in the West Glamorgan Youth Orchestra and through that became familiar with the more common classical pieces; but, as with any other areas of my musical taste, I love to explore the outskirts too.

It's in the DNA of the Proms that the familiar sits side by side with the new and undiscovered, so you can go along and reignite a perhaps fading enthusiasm for core repertoire, like Tchaikovsky's Violin Concerto (which I saw Joshua Bell bring to new life at the Proms in 2013), as well as discover more unfamiliar repertoire or even, my favourite, witness the excitement of the first outing of a never-before-performed piece.

A night out at the Royal Albert Hall is never anything but an occasion. Even listening at home on BBC Radio 3, the sense of the moment is ever present.

> **"I'd introduce an All Nations Day to celebrate the uniqueness of Britain's four corners."**

After all, a venue built as a token of love has its own particular enchantment, and performers and listeners feel this magic.

My fantasy Prom would be a trio formed of cellist Pierre Fournier, violinist David Oistrakh and pianist Arthur Rubinstein. In the 'real' world, I'd go for Martha Argerich with solo Bach, then joined by Patricia Kopatchinskaja (violin) and Alisa Weilerstein (cello). It would be Schubert's Piano Trio No. 2, with a second half of *Memoryhouse* by Max Richter, performed by the LSO under Sir Simon Rattle. I'd also love to introduce an All Nations Day to the last day of the Proms, to celebrate the uniqueness of every corner of Great Britain. ●

Favourite composer: J. S. Bach – and a whole list of performers of his music: Karl Richter, Dinu Lipati, Arthur Grumiaux, Artur Schnabel …

Most recent musical 'discovery': Max Richter's *Sleep*. The surprise, listening to it through the night on Radio 3, was the feeling of brotherhood with listeners across the world.

Proms 2016 highlight: Prokofiev's *Alexander Nevsky* (Prom 1). Having seen the film recently, it'll be interesting to hear the music in its cantata form. There's also a whole lot of shakin' going on in Bernstein's 'Mambo' from *West Side Story* at the Ten Pieces II Proms (Proms 10 & 12).

GOLDEN RECORD

Conductor Bernard Haitink has appeared in almost every BBC Proms festival since his debut here in 1966. He looks back over 50 years of performances, orchestras and audiences with **Fiona Maddocks**

Half a century ago, on 22 August 1966, Bernard Haitink made his first appearance at the BBC Proms. London was swinging. England had just won the World Cup, Twiggy was face of the year and The Beatles were about to give their last concert. The quiet-mannered but determined young Dutchman, only in his thirties but already Chief Conductor of the Royal Concertgebouw Orchestra in Amsterdam, had other musical preoccupations: the great symphonies of Bruckner and Mahler, hardly known to audiences in Britain at the time. For his Proms debut he conducted the BBC Symphony Orchestra in Bruckner's Seventh Symphony. It was only the fourth time the work had been heard in the festival's history. That seminal performance helped to kick-start a new and unstoppable interest in the Austrian composer, especially at the Proms.

So successful was Haitink's debut that the following year he was back with not one but four Royal Albert Hall engagements, including his first Mahler at the Proms: the 'Resurrection' Symphony – even more of a rarity than the Bruckner. By then, as principal conductor of the London Philharmonic Orchestra, Haitink was a familiar face in the UK. Over the next few years, Mahler symphonies tumbled onto the Proms programme, sometimes conducted by Haitink with various orchestras, sometimes by others with the Mahler bug, his music rapidly burning itself on the consciousness of a fresh generation of audiences hungry for these visionary works.

Haitink has a vivid memory of that early Mahler 2: chiefly of being dazed and nervous, which he says he still is when he conducts a Prom. He remembers looking not down into the Arena, but out to the back of the Hall and being amazed by the sheer size of it. 'And afterwards sensing the warmth of the Prommers, being knocked backwards by it.' Touchingly he says he still feels the same every time and he just wants to thank the Prommers for their dedicated listening and support.

'The Royal Albert Hall is such a special place. I've seen soloists come to it for the first time and they look at that huge space and can't believe that, later that evening, it will be full. It's totally unique. As a foreigner I can say that! I started listening to the Proms in the 1940s, when it was forbidden [during the Nazi occupation of the Netherlands]. The Proms had nights dedicated to one composer. I remember conductors like Basil Cameron [who conducted more than 400 Proms between 1941 and 1964]. That's a long time ago …'

For his 50th-anniversary Prom, Haitink will conduct Mahler's Symphony No. 3 – at around 100 minutes, one of the longest symphonies in

German troops entering Amsterdam on 16 May 1940, the day after Dutch forces had surrendered, following the bombing of Rotterdam. Although foreign broadcasts were prohibited during the occupation, which lasted until 1945, the teenaged Haitink listened to Proms concerts on the radio

> **Haitink just wants to thank the Prommers for their dedicated listening and support.**

the mainstream repertoire. By this time Haitink will be 87. Lithe though he is, he will need every ounce of stamina. Was this epic work – requiring an alto soloist, a boys' choir, women's voices and a colossal orchestra, and encompassing a majestic vision of every aspect of creation – his choice? 'Well, not really. But they asked and I couldn't say no,' Haitink replies with a laconic smile.

'Mahler's Third is in many ways a very spectacular piece,' he reflects. 'It is so diverse. The first movement is the difficult one, especially for an audience that doesn't know it well. It's nearly half an hour long. There are many people at the Proms who are new to the festival, new to music … I hope they will try it. After that it becomes very fascinating and idyllic, with the horn solo and the posthorn. And then there's the wonderful last-movement Adagio. It's Mahler at his best, one of the most beautiful things he ever wrote. And as a performer you don't make it too sentimental. That's another thing. He was not a happy man. He was always trying to achieve things and

made tremendous enemies, especially in Vienna, at the time a city full of intrigues …'

Don't ask Haitink to choose between Mahler and Bruckner. He still holds both composers passionately close to his heart. How would he characterise the difference between the pair, once often mentioned in the same breath as grand, late-Romantic symphonists in the Austrian tradition? Haitink takes a very long pause. His answer, characteristically modest but penetrating, is worth the wait. 'I will make it extremely simple, if perhaps a bit stupid. Bruckner is a mountain. Mahler is sometimes hell. Bruckner is a steady ascent. Mahler's

Image Bank WW2/NIOD

WORKING WITH BERNARD HAITINK

London Symphony Orchestra percussionist David Jackson gives a player's perspective on performing with Bernard Haitink

There is always a real sense of occasion whenever a period of work with Bernard Haitink comes up in the London Symphony Orchestra diary. I grew up listening to his great recordings, most notably with the Royal Concertgebouw Orchestra, of the works with which he is most often associated – symphonic works by Bruckner, Mozart, Beethoven and of course Mahler. His skill in judging the pace and tread of some of these huge pieces is something that, for me, sets him apart from other interpreters.

Haitink is a disarmingly charming gentleman to work with; a life of facing expectant musicians has also imbued him with an endearing sense of humour. As the LSO embarked on rehearsals for Mahler's huge Sixth Symphony a few years ago, he greeted us with 'Ladies and gentlemen, this is a long piece!'. Then a wry smile … 'Let's not make it longer than necessary!'

In rehearsal he is a man of few words – just the occasional balance note here or articulation query there. The years may have diminished his apparent physical energy on the rostrum, but there's no denying the latent power that he still conjures when required.

It always feels that we work 'with' Haitink – he 'invites' you to play. He possesses an amazing quality of allowing space in which the orchestra can make the music live. That's not to say that he's not always in control, but the confidence he inspires with the clarity of his gestures means that players can produce their very best sound and musical meanings exactly when they are required. That, in part, is why I feel the whole orchestra sounds different for Haitink. In over 20 years of playing with the LSO, I have rarely cherished musical experiences and memories more than when Bernard Haitink has been at the centre of the orchestra.

He also has the distinction of having one of the greatest anagrams of his name in the music business: Bernard Haitink – A drink in the bar!

music is down there in the depths and sometimes, somehow it climbs up to the peaks.'

Born in Amsterdam in 1929, studying first as a violinist before switching to conducting, Haitink started early with Mahler, but didn't immediately take to it. 'Strangely enough, Mahler came quite soon when I started conducting. More strangely, I didn't like it at all at that time! I was more at home with Bruckner – that was quite odd for a young man. I loved French music too. Mahler wasn't allowed to be played in Amsterdam during the Nazi occupation.' Before 1940, there was already a long tradition of Mahler performance in the city and a huge audience for the composer. The conductor Willem Mengelberg (1871–1951), a friend of Mahler and a predecessor to Haitink at the Royal Concertgebouw Orchestra, had introduced the music to the Dutch and instituted a Mahler festival in 1920.

'So, Mahler was an important figure. But between the ages of 11 and 16 I wasn't able to listen to his music – until the war ended in 1945. I still went to concerts, even if my parents didn't like it, because the majority of the audience were German officers. But I had a violin teacher in the orchestra who said to them, "The boy must listen to music," and he smuggled me in. Life, musical life, slowly recovered after the war. There was none of that earlier Mahler tradition left, for the public or for the musicians. It was a new thing, more or less. I heard a little of his music here and there: Symphonies No. 2 and No. 1. But the Ninth, the Seventh and the Sixth were totally unknown – they came later. This was when I was still in my teens.'

The turning point in Haitink's professional life, and in his relationship with Mahler, came early: in 1957, when he was appointed Chief Conductor of the Royal Concertgebouw Orchestra. 'It was unexpected. I became the conductor of a famous orchestra far too early. Then I was catapulted into a prominent position where, at that time, orchestras still had enormous recording contracts that had to be fulfilled. I think it was 30 recordings a year! They said they would like me to record a Mahler cycle. I said, "Oh my God!" And they said it would have to be done in two years! I became rebellious. I said, "No way!"'

Haitink requested that only one symphony was recorded each year. 'And I said I must perform each symphony at least three or four times,

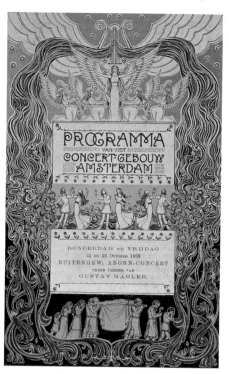

A programme from October 1903, when Mahler conducted his Third Symphony at the Amsterdam Concertgebouw, at the invitation of conductor Willem Mengelberg

Bernard Haitink in rehearsal at the Usher Hall for the 1978 Edinburgh International Festival

because it was totally unknown territory for me. So every season we did a Mahler symphony, for a few performances, which were recorded. It took 10 years! Then there was the Bruckner cycle, too, at the same time, so you can imagine how that felt. This was the late 1950s and into the 1960s. For the Mahler I first did Symphonies Nos. 1, 2, 4 and 5. The others were difficult for me and I tackled them after. Don't ask me how, but somehow we did it in the end.'

Haitink's own preparation of the score has always been and remains remarkably straightforward. 'How does one prepare? One opens the score. And one struggles through it, again and again.

I conduct with a score. Without one you are asking for trouble. You make mistakes. It can happen to all of us, however well you know something.' He adds, as an afterthought, 'But I'm really too old for these pieces.' That seems impossible. His concert diary is full. He and his wife Patricia have just moved from Lucerne to London, handily placed for the Royal Albert Hall. Evidently he thrives on hard work.

'Well, it becomes critical. These are very long pieces. I do stand to conduct but it becomes difficult. I have a bar stool I can sit on between movements. But conductors are lucky. It's hard to play an instrument at a great age. Conductors seem able to go on longer. Klemperer in old age moved in such a minimal, particular way, yet it worked. It's a matter of personality. The strange mystery of this conducting business is that you feel better when you are doing it than when you are not. It's the concentration, the contact with people, the constant self-questioning – how do I do this piece, how do I rehearse it? These are important things. It keeps you busy. I love musicians. I love orchestral musicians.'

Haitink still gives his revered conducting masterclasses in Lucerne. Above all, he has one golden rule. 'I always tell the students, if something goes wrong, there's an 80 per cent chance that it's your fault, not your players. If, say, after the first two chords of the 'Eroica', the conductor stops to talk about Beethoven and his life and times and Napoleon and a short history of the French Revolution … forget it! Don't talk so much. Just conduct the music.' ●

Chief Music Critic of *The Observer*, Fiona Maddocks was founder-editor of *BBC Music Magazine*. She is the author of a biography of Hildegard of Bingen and of *Harrison Birtwistle: Wild Tracks*, a conversation diary.

BERNARD HAITINK: 50 YEARS AT THE BBC PROMS

87 Proms appearances to date, conducting 13 orchestras
33 with the London Philharmonic Orchestra
14 with the BBC Symphony Orchestra
14 with the Royal Concertgebouw Orchestra
5 with the European Union Youth Orchestra
4 with the London Symphony Orchestra
3 with the Chamber Orchestra of Europe
2 with the Berlin Philharmonic
2 with the Boston Symphony Orchestra
2 with the Chicago Symphony Orchestra
2 with the Dresden Staatskapelle
2 with the Orchestra of the Royal Opera House
2 with the Philharmonia Orchestra
2 with the Vienna Philharmonic

Proms performances include
17 Bruckner symphonies
16 Mahler symphonies
13 Operas: Bizet *Carmen* (1985); Debussy *Pelléas et Mélisande* (1976); Haydn *La fedeltà premiata* (1979); Mozart *Così fan tutte* (1978), *Don Giovanni* (1977), *The Magic Flute* (1973, 1980), *The Marriage of Figaro* (1984); Verdi *Don Carlos* (1996), *Falstaff* (1988), *Simon Boccanegra* (1986), *La traviata* (1987); Stravinsky *The Rake's Progress* (1975)

Large-scale choral works include
Britten's *War Requiem* (1976); Beethoven's *Missa solemnis* for Haitink's only appearance at the First Night of the Proms (1997)

Proms with soloists including
Singers Thomas Allen, Elly Ameling, Janet Baker, Maria Ewing, Dmitri Hvorostovsky, Peter Pears

Violinists Norbert Brainin, Rodney Friend, Ida Haendel, Thomas Zehetmair

Pianists Emanuel Ax, Alfred Brendel, Clifford Curzon, Hélène Grimaud, Murray Perahia, Maria João Pires

Bernard Haitink at the Proms
Mahler Symphony No. 3
PROM 18 • 29 JULY

RUSSIAN HEROES

As two great Russian nationalistic works appear in the opening weekend of the Proms,
Daniel Jaffé introduces the historic rulers Alexander Nevsky and Boris Godunov – whose dramatic
lives of battle and political intrigue fuelled the imaginations of Sergey Prokofiev and Modest Mussorgsky

It is a truism that Russians have a great love of their literature, and know – at least in outline – their nation's history. Russian composers in turn have been able to count on their audience's familiarity with the histories or novels on which their work is based – as for example with Prokofiev's operatic adaptation of Leo Tolstoy's *War and Peace* or Mussorgsky's adaptation of Alexander Pushkin's *Boris Godunov*. Paradoxically, one of Russia's earliest heroes, the 13th-century warrior prince Alexander Nevsky (*c*1220–63), gained iconic status even before Russia had a literary tradition: he was defined for Russians – and indeed for those further afield – as recently as 1938 by Sergey Eisenstein's landmark film and by the celebrated cantata created from its soundtrack by its composer, Prokofiev.

Alexander Nevsky gained enduring fame in July 1240 when he defeated the Swedes on the Neva River – hence the epithet 'Nevsky' given to him two centuries after that victory, when

> " Eisenstein confessed he chose Alexander Nevsky as a subject since 'nobody knows much about him, so nobody could possibly find fault with me'. "

he was canonised by Ivan IV (Ivan the Terrible, coincidentally the subject of Eisenstein's and Prokofiev's next cinematic masterpiece). The following year, Alexander – having abdicated as Prince of Novgorod following a disagreement with the city's boyars – was

persuaded to return and defend his people against the invading Teutonic Knights. Alexander and his army drove the Knights into German-held Estonia. There, on the frozen Lake Chud, the northernmost and largest of the three lakes of Peipus, he defeated the Knights in the so-called 'Battle on the Ice', famously depicted in Eisenstein's film.

Eisenstein later confessed that he chose Alexander Nevsky as his subject, at the height of Stalin's cultural purge, since 'nobody knows much about him, and so nobody could possibly find fault with me'. Eisenstein's implicit brief in 1938 was to create a morale-raising film, which would address the growing menace of Nazi Germany by drawing a parallel with the medieval Teutonic Knights defeated by Alexander and his army. Eisenstein's *Alexander Nevsky* is in more than one sense a black-and-white film: Alexander himself is decisive, fearless yet warm and avuncular to his followers – in short, the perfect Stalinist hero – while the Teutonic Knights are caricature villains who toss innocent young children into a bonfire and mercilessly mow down civilians when sacking the city of Pskov.

Prokofiev's music directly reflects this. Most obviously, for the villainous Knights he fashioned a crude and sinister chant, rejecting authentic medieval plainsong as 'far too remote and emotionally alien to us to be able to stimulate the imagination of the present-day film spectator'. Yet he goes further, as the actual *sound* of his music reflects the film's black-and-white quality. Prokofiev deliberately restrains his usually highly colourful orchestral style – evident in then recent scores such as his ballet *Romeo and Juliet* – to create a sombre, 'black-and-white' palette which harmonises with Eisenstein's use of a deliberately simplified

Risen to power but racked by guilt: Mikhail Kazakov as Boris Godunov in a Bolshoi Opera production at the Royal Opera House, Covent Garden, 2006

visual and narrative style, appropriate for the retelling of an ancient epic. The occasional glint of percussive instruments, such as anvil and xylophone, is therefore thrown into sharp relief, reaching its fullest sonic splendour in the cantata's final chorus. Perhaps the boldest contrast, though, occurs at the culminating 'Battle on the Ice', where the Teutonic Knights' baleful music, all in the bass-register, is suddenly overthrown by major-key music 'brightened', as Prokofiev described it, 'like a meteor' by high strings accompanied by even

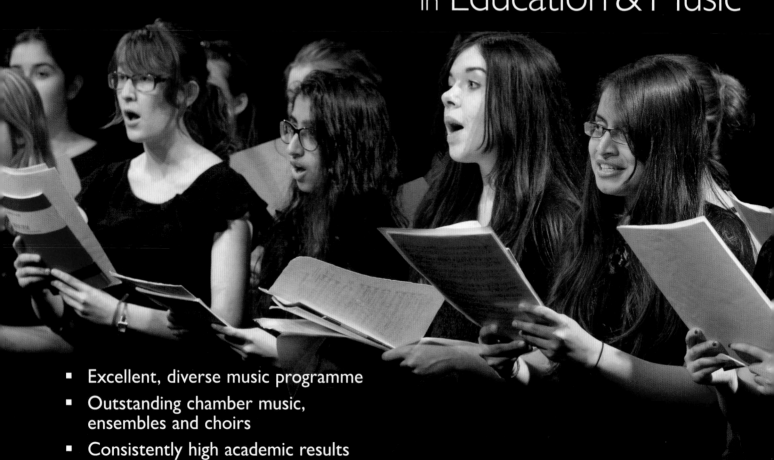

Excellence
in Education & Music

- Excellent, diverse music programme
- Outstanding chamber music, ensembles and choirs
- Consistently high academic results
- Generous music scholarships
- Academic scholarships and bursaries
- Choice of A Level or IB Diploma

An independent school for girls aged 4-18

For further information, please visit
www.nlcs.org.uk

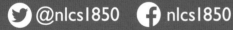 @nlcs1850   nlcs1850

North London
Collegiate School
Founded 1850

higher woodwind trilling and chattering, while the Russians drive the Knights to their watery demise.

Prokofiev also adds an appropriately 'historic' sheen through allusions to the operas of Mussorgsky and Borodin, both in his choruses and, most obviously, in the mezzo-soprano lament, 'The Field of the Dead'. It is perhaps a tribute to Prokofiev's art that despite this stylistic affinity, *Boris* is yet more 'modern' and sophisticated in sensibility, befitting a drama of some psychological subtlety.

Little evidence has survived to explain what first attracted Mussorgsky to the Pushkin drama on which his opera is based. But it seems likely that Mussorgsky's close friend, the historian Vladimir Nikolsky, not only assisted but also directly instigated the creation of *Boris Godunov*. Boris was one of Ivan the Terrible's most trusted advisors; his sister married Ivan's mentally feeble son, Fyodor I, who eventually became tsar in 1584, with Boris effectively the power behind the throne. By 1598, when Boris succeeded Fyodor (who had died without a male heir), he was an experienced and able administrator. However, his reign was dogged by ill luck, most particularly a catastrophic crop failure in the autumn of 1601, which presaged a devastating three-year famine. A belief soon took root among the Russian peasantry that God was punishing them because of their ruler's alleged misdeeds. There was growing support for a young pretender from Poland as he marched upon Moscow, claiming to be a true heir, Dmitry.

The real-life Dmitry was Fyodor's half-brother, who in 1591, aged 9, was found dead with a knife wound to the neck. Dmitry's mother, Maria Nagaia, had accused Boris of having plotted his murder, yet Godunov's guilt was never established. Still, suspicion of Godunov's machinations for the throne lingered on and was fruitfully exploited by those intent on deposing him – and again, some 220 years later, by Pushkin in his drama *Boris Godunov*, written in 1825.

Pushkin's and Mussorgsky's Boris is a character of Shakespearean complexity, doomed by a single crime and unable to redeem himself either through benevolent rule over his subjects or through loving kindness to his family. Mussorgsky's aim was to capture the individuality and essence of every protagonist he portrayed. *Boris Godunov* is, therefore, a more nuanced and 'colourful' work than *Alexander Nevsky*, involving not only a richer palette in terms of instrumental timbre, but also a more daring and disconcerting range of dissonances: while Prokofiev reserves the most grating sounds in *Alexander* for the 'baddies', Mussorgsky uses dislocated harmonies and searing chromaticism to capture the psychological torment of his anti-hero. Boris is, in short, one of the greatest tragic creations in all music. ●

Daniel Jaffé is the author of *Sergey Prokofiev*, published as part of Phaidon's 20th-Century Composers series, and has published the *Historical Dictionary of Russian Music*. He has lectured and broadcast extensively on Russian music, including on BBC Radio 3 and BBC Four.

Prokofiev Alexander Nevsky – cantata

PROM 1 • 15 JULY

Mussorgsky Boris Godunov (original version, 1869)

PROM 2 • 16 JULY

TWO RUSSIAN HEROES

Alexander Nevsky (c1220–1263)

Prince of Novgorod, 1236–52
Grand Prince of Vladimir, 1252–63
Subject of Sergei Eisenstein's 1938 film
(score and cantata by Sergey Prokofiev, 1891–1953)

Eisenstein on Prokofiev:
'[He] is not only one of the greatest composers of our time, but also, in my opinion, the most wonderful film composer.'

Boris Godunov (c1551–1605)

Tsar of Russia, 1598–1605
Subject of Pushkin's drama (1825) and Mussorgsky's opera (1869, rev. 1872)

Scholar Richard Taruskin on 'Boris Godunov':
'We are made to "see" musically into Boris's soul, and are made so painfully aware of the tsar's predicament that we seem to experience it along with him.'

THE TENTH
ENGLISH MUSIC FESTIVAL

26-30 MAY 2016
DORCHESTER-ON-THAMES, OXFORDSHIRE

The English Music Festival celebrates its tenth anniversary with a thrilling programme of World Première performances of major twentieth-century British composers, overlooked masterpieces and much-loved favourites from artists including the BBC Concert Orchestra, English Symphony Orchestra and rising-star mezzo Kathryn Rudge. Events range from early music from The Queen's Six, through the World Première of a major work by Ralph Vaughan Williams, to the toe-tapping New Foxtrot Serenaders, as well as the complete extant music by George Butterworth, on the centenary of his death, in conjunction with Radley College. Join us for the most exhilarating EMF yet!

For further information contact Festival Director Em Marshall-Luck at em.marshall-luck@englishmusicfestival.org.uk or the EMF Information Line on 01535 272054.

www.englishmusicfestival.org.uk

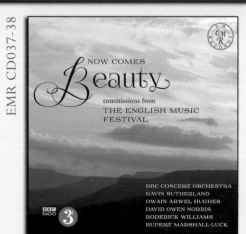

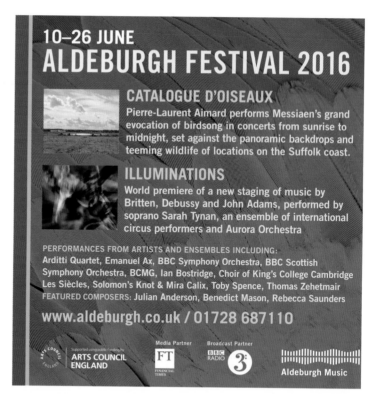

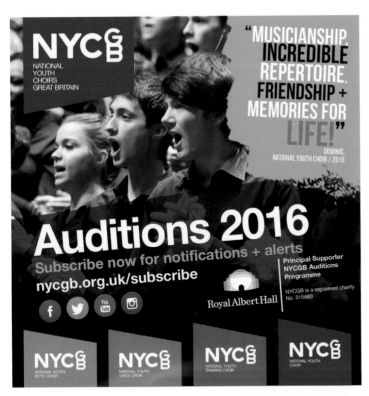

EDINBURGH INTERNATIONAL FESTIVAL

5–29 AUGUST

GREAT ARTISTS, GREAT MUSIC
INSPIRING EXPERIENCES IN
EDINBURGH THIS AUGUST

Highlights include **Maxim Vengerov**, **Minnesota Orchestra**, **Swedish Radio Symphony Orchestra**, **Mikhail Pletnev and Russian National Orchestra**, **Danill Trifonov**, **Magdalena Kožená**, **Sir Antonio Pappano and Orchestra dell'Accademia Nazionale di Santa Cecilia**, **Pierre-Laurent Aimard**, **Marin Alsop and São Paolo Symphony Orchestra**, **George Li**, **Yannick Nézet-Séguin and Rotterdam Philharmonic Orchestra** and many more.

EIF.CO.UK

#EDINTFEST

·EDINBVRGH·
THE CITY OF EDINBURGH COUNCIL

Charity No SC004694

CREATIVE SCOT LAND
ALBA | CHRUTHACHAIL

THE POWER OF ENCHANTMENT

Although the radiant harmonies and sensual colours of Henri Dutilleux's music follow in his native French tradition of Debussy and Ravel, he sought an individual path. As the Proms celebrates the centenary of his birth, **Caroline Rae** explores Dutilleux's distinctive sound-world

A mong the most widely acclaimed and accessible composers of our time, Henri Dutilleux ranks among the greats of French music. Born in 1916 and blessed with a longevity that enabled him to remain active well into his nineties, Dutilleux completed a series of carefully crafted masterworks that are performed throughout the world. In the year he would have turned 100 – he died in May 2013 – his music is being celebrated across the globe from Los Angeles to Tokyo as well as in London, Paris and New York.

Dutilleux's music is often described in terms of luxuriant orchestral colourism, harmonic sensuality and the exploration of sound as timbre – attributes considered characteristically French, and ones that make him heir to a musical tradition stemming from Debussy and Ravel. Borrowing a title from one of Ravel's early works, Dutilleux used the expression 'sites auriculaires' – points of beauty for the ear – to suggest the role of sound-colour as an inspirational force, and spoke of the 'magic of timbre' as being among the most important qualities of a composer. Other 20th- and 21st-century French composers have demonstrated similar fascinations for sound as timbre, including Messiaen, Boulez and the 'Spectralist' composers such as Tristan Murail and Gérard Grisey, who transformed acoustic musical sound through computer analysis as a means of synthesising new sound-spectra. Dutilleux's exploration of transformative instrumental textures and sound-colour in his seminal orchestral work *Métaboles* (1959–64) provided a point of compositional departure for the Spectralists, especially Grisey. Through extending the variation techniques first explored in his Piano Sonata (1946–8), the work that was Dutilleux's self-declared Op. 1, and subsequently expanded through processes of continuous motivic development or progressive growth in his First and Second Symphonies (1950–51 and 1955–9), *Métaboles* defined him unequivocally as a composer of innovation. It was also *Métaboles* that, in 1989, was the first of Dutilleux's works to be performed at the Proms.

Another clue to the kernel of Dutilleux's compositional *raison d'être* appears in what he described as the 'power of enchantment', a timbral magic that seduces the ear even after sound itself has dissipated into silence. Such an evocative objective resonates with the music of his predecessor Debussy, for whom moments of poignant silence were also as important as sound itself. The most direct expression of Dutilleux's music is thus one that beguiles through exploring new combinations of instrumental

Anne Frank, to whom the central movement of *The Shadows of Time* is dedicated, along with 'all children who died innocently between 1945 and 1995'

texture and sonority that parallel the ways painters in 20th-century France sought new means of depicting light and blending colour.

Yet, although Dutilleux is a towering figure of what might be called the French tradition – in terms of the roots from which his music has grown and in relation to the sources that inspired his work from the visual arts and literature, particularly Baudelaire – he disliked being described as a quintessentially French composer. Dutilleux cited the leavening of his compositional *métier* to include foreign influences and looked as much towards the music of Central and Eastern Europe as to his homeland. Like many French composers, not least Ravel, he admired the Russians. But there was a deeper reason for Dutilleux's attraction to a wider scope of influences; his maternal grandfather, a distinguished musician in his own right, was of Polish origin. Dutilleux often remarked on the aesthetic kinship between Polish and French composers and felt close to the music of Chopin; the connection also cemented a life-long friendship with the composer Witold Lutosławski.

Although Dutilleux remarked that fundamentally he was not an atonal composer, despite his intensely chromatic language, he occasionally experimented with 12-note ideas and was attracted to certain works by Schoenberg and Berg, as he found that they too demonstrated similar preoccupations with the transparency and refinement of timbre. The influence of Berg is particularly redolent in both Dutilleux's cello concerto '*Tout un monde lointain …*' (1967–70) and in *The Shadows of Time* (1995–7), while the final song, 'Enivrez-vous', of his last completed work, *Le temps l'horloge* (2006–9), briefly paraphrases the moment in Berg's opera of Wozzeck's drowning.

DUTILLEUX, MY TEACHER

Composer Kenneth Hesketh recalls the liberating effect of studying with Henri Dutilleux

In 1995 I attended the Tanglewood Music Center in America, where I was fortunate enough to work with Henri Dutilleux. His presence generated a warm, open-natured camaraderie and he showed great understanding of each young composer's aesthetic stance.

Dutilleux lectured on his own music and that of composers he found interesting (from Berlioz to the musicological thoughts of his former student Francis Bayer). His one-to-one lessons were wonderful, usually accompanied by a bottle of excellent wine and an ability to listen and comment with great precision on a compositional problem.

During one evening dinner, he and I went outside to smoke and, during a conversation on composer development, he said, 'Il faut tuer le père' (One must kill one's father). I took it to mean that one must not be afraid to move beyond comfortable but dominating influences, to not feel hampered by the past. I had a sense that this was of deep personal meaning to Dutilleux in his own development.

Dutilleux's compositional approach was revealed in an exchange with the American composer George Perle. Perle approached post-tonal harmony in a more intensely systematised way than Dutilleux, who achieved harmonic consistency in a far more fluid manner and with greater freedom and use of materials. Dutilleux's work has particular rules of construction, but always allows for the improvisatory, spontaneous moment. His method exhibited a great humanity and sense of enchantment that was intensely interesting and liberating for me.

Dutilleux also admired Schumann, especially the songs, in which he immersed himself while composing *Correspondances* (2002–4) and *Le temps l'horloge*. These vocal works crowned the Indian summer of Dutilleux's final years.

So what of Dutilleux's quest for the power of enchantment and can his timbral magic be defined? The orchestral works represented in

this year's Proms, '*Tout un monde lointain …*', *Timbres, espace, mouvement* (1976–8, rev. 1990) and *The Shadows of Time*, demonstrate the essence of his unique sound-world. Shimmering orchestration, subtle blending of percussive effects, resonant bell-like textures and the progressive expansion of intervals into wide harmonic spaces that juxtapose extremes of registers – all create an environment that seamlessly combines rhythmic drive with intense expressivity. In '*Tout un monde lointain …*' the power of enchantment is evoked at the end of the central movement, 'Houles', where an ascending flourish on the solo cello evaporates into whispered interpolations on crotales, flute and suspended cymbal before transforming into ethereal harmonics on the harp punctuated with a gong. While these textures owe much to the wisps of sound at the end of 'Jeux de vagues' in Debussy's *La mer*, the final moments of the concerto as a whole recall

> ❝ Dutilleux spoke of the 'magic of timbre' as being among the most important qualities of a composer. ❞

Berg's *Lyric Suite*; the work ends inconclusively (without a double bar) as an oscillating figure on solo cello slips breathlessly into silence.

The tripartite title of *Timbres, espace, mouvement*, a work that receives its Proms premiere this year, reflects the three main elements central to Dutilleux's compositional thinking: colour, harmonic space and rhythmic impulsion. The importance of colour in particular is asserted through musical allusions to the painting that inspired the work, Van Gogh's *The Starry Night*. Transforming the painter's palette into sound, dark orchestral colours are juxtaposed with flashes of brilliant, swirling light in Dutilleux's writing for wind and percussion, while static episodes alternate with passages of almost violent energy to suggest the whirling clouds of Van Gogh's anguished night sky.

Composed nearly 20 years later, when Dutilleux had turned 80, *The Shadows of Time* represents both continuity and new development. Feeling he had neglected the human voice, Dutilleux began to make amends through adding children's voices to the central movement dedicated to the memory of Anne Frank. Tragic in mood, this work is among Dutilleux's most sombre contemplations on the human condition. The orchestration is dark and brooding, the predominance of low strings contrasting with what he called the metallic glare of wind instruments – another facet of Dutilleux's magic of timbre.

Centenaries often provide a useful opportunity for reflecting on a composer's legacy. In the case of Dutilleux, who was still among us only three years ago, his influence continues to evolve, as does the significance of his compositional achievement. While the death of a composer may be followed by a period of neglect, there has been no abating of interest in the work of Dutilleux, whose music is set to endure through its sheer beauty of sound and power of enchantment. ●

Caroline Rae is a pianist and Reader in Music at Cardiff University, and first met Dutilleux during her student years. She has published widely on French music since Debussy and broadcasts regularly on BBC Radio 3.

Detail from *The Starry Night* (1889) by Vincent Van Gogh (1853–90). Its brilliant, swirling palette of colours is realised in the music of Dutilleux's *Timbres, espace, mouvement*

Ainsi la nuit
PROMS CHAMBER MUSIC 1 • 18 JULY

The Shadows of Time
PROM 32 • 8 AUGUST

'Tout un monde lointain …'
PROM 33 • 9 AUGUST

Timbres, espace, mouvement
PROM 34 • 10 AUGUST

MY PROMS
FIONA SHAW

actor, director

I remember standing as a Prommer and adoring it. I used to go before I even went to RADA, so I was hanging around London, over-staying my welcome on people's floors and doing bits of temp work. I would go down with little picnics, queueing up with a boy called Bill and bathing in the lovely sunshine around the side of the Royal Albert Hall. It was quite heady. Hyde Park was a real place for the young and the poor to hang out. And the Albert Hall! I came from Ireland and I'd never seen anything remotely that big in my life! But the fact that it was available to young people was very valuable, as it is now: a wonderful thing.

I first performed at the Proms as St Joan in Honegger's *Joan of Arc at the Stake* in 1997. When you perform at the RAH, it changes your relationship to the place entirely. I have great memories of rehearsing for that Prom but I do remember being awfully terrified when I realised what we had let ourselves in

> **When you perform at the RAH, it changes your relationship to the place entirely.**

for! I was standing in the middle of the Arena with this absolutely vast choir, and with the conductor behind me.

This year there's some beautiful Fauré with King's College Choir that I'm looking forward to. There's also the gorgeous Poulenc *Stabat mater*. I always think Poulenc only wrote about three tunes, but he wrote them all so brilliantly! ●

Favourite performer: Allan Clayton (tenor) is to me a revelation. He refuses to allow the conductor or the composer to be the only person telling the story. He's going to sing Brett Dean's *Hamlet* at Glyndebourne next year: I think he should *act* Hamlet, because of his ability to be and to think in the moment.

Most recent musical 'discovery': Hans Werner Henze. Before directing his opera *Elegy for Young Lovers* I thought I couldn't 'hear' this music at all. I was in Los Angeles and I asked composer Tom Adès to come round and explain this music to me. Within about 50 bars I began to hear so many other composers. I could hear 19th-century Romanticism brilliantly thwarted, like the tributary of a river being sent in a new direction.

Proms 2016 highlight: Janáček's *The Makropulos Affair* (Prom 45) for the theatricality of it. But Mozart's Mass in C minor (Prom 46) is a rare treat too.

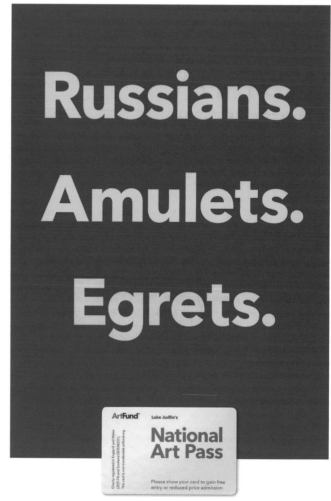

UNIVERSITY OF
WEST LONDON
London College of Music

London College of Music is an internationally recognised music institution with a long tradition of providing innovative and creative courses. Many courses are specifically designed to fit around personal and professional commitments and are offered on a full or part time basis.

Our well established industry links and professional partnerships in London, the UK and abroad ensure that your studies are real and relevant to your musical interests.

UNDERGRADUATE PORTFOLIO:
- Composition
- Music Management
- Music Technology
- Musical Theatre
- Performance

POSTGRADUATE PORTFOLIO:
- Composition
- Music Management
- Music Technology
- Musical Theatre
- Performance

→ London College of Music Examinations offer a wide range of external graded exams and diplomas.
uwl.ac.uk/lcmexams

 ENGLISH CHAMBER ORCHESTRA

uwl.ac.uk/lcm

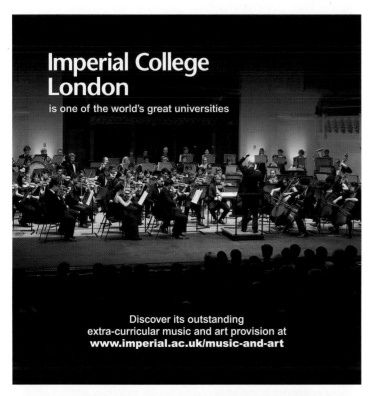
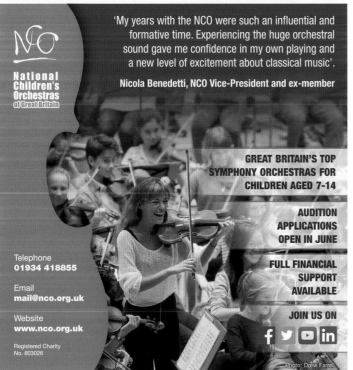

Talented Dancer or Musician?

Yes, TALENT is ALL you need for a place at a Music and Dance School.

All our schools are dedicated to encouraging talented young people from all financial and cultural backgrounds... we can offer up to 100% Government funding for places.

Music and Dance Schools are committed to the highest teaching standards in music and dance, as well as an excellent academic education.

If you are interested in one of the Music and Dance Schools just visit our website for contact details.

There are nine Music and Dance Schools throughout the UK

- Chetham's School of Music, Manchester
- Elmhurst School for Dance, Birmingham
- St Mary's Music School, Edinburgh
- The Hammond, Chester
- The Purcell School for Young Musicians, Herts
- The Royal Ballet School, London
- Tring Park School for the Performing Arts, Herts
- Wells Cathedral School, Somerset
- Yehudi Menuhin School, Surrey

www.musicanddanceschools.com

MUSIC
& DANCE
SCHOOLS
ACCESS TO EXCELLENCE

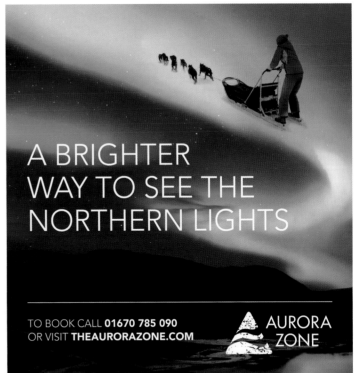

PROMS EXTRA

The Proms has always aimed to take the greatest classical music to the widest possible audience. But, in addition to the 93 concerts this year, there's an equally diverse range of talks, composer events and films – all designed to bring you closer to the music

Proms Extra is a series of free daily events designed to enhance your Proms experience – including workshops, talks and film screenings as well as participation events for all ages and musical abilities. (For our range of events aimed specifically at families, *see pages 68–71*.) The series gives unparalleled access to the wealth of musicians, composers and musical experts that help create the Proms. All of the events are designed to give you a new and engaging insight into the concert you are about to hear, whether exploring a specific piece or the cultural and historical context of the music.

This summer Proms Extra takes place at Imperial College Union, just across the road from the Royal Albert Hall. (*For more information on Imperial College Union, see page 160.*)

Most of the events are recorded by BBC Radio 3 and broadcast during the interval of the main-evening concert, and there are also a number of complete radio programmes recorded at the series this summer: these include Radio 3's *In Tune* on the First Night (15 July), an edition of *The Listening Service* with Tom Service (17 July), the 2016 final of Radio 4's music quiz *Counterpoint*, marking the show's 30th anniversary (2 September), and a Last Night of the Proms edition of Radio 3's *The Choir* (10 September).

All Proms Extra events are free of charge and most are unticketed, with the exception of the radio programmes (15 & 17 July, 15 August, 2 & 10 September), for which free tickets are available from BBC Studio Audiences – visit bbc.co.uk/showsandtours. Seating at Imperial College Union is limited so we recommend arriving early.

Chris Christodoulou/BBC/Proms Sing!

PROMS EXTRA TALKS

Who better to introduce you to the music of the evening's performance than a line-up of Radio 3 presenters and musical and cultural experts. Get more out of your whole Proms experience – you'll hear the music with different ears. But it's not just about the music. A number of events add context by exploring literary or historical themes. So, marking the 400th anniversary of the death of William Shakespeare, there's a series in which leading figures discuss their professions as depicted in Shakespeare's plays. We also celebrate the birthdays of Charlotte Brontë, H. G. Wells and Capability Brown, as well as the 350th anniversary of the Great Fire of London. And on 16 July, Frank Cotrell-Boyce, writer of the 2012 Olympics Opening Ceremony, reflects on the cultural legacy of the Games and the importance of the arts in society.

COMPOSERS IN CONVERSATION

New music has long been a mainstay of the Proms, and this summer sees 30 commissions and premieres, as well as other works by living composers. Across the season we'll be celebrating some of the featured composers, offering insight into their work and discussing their influences. Several of the events feature live performances by students from UK conservatories.

Anthony Payne • 26 JULY, 5.45PM
Helen Grime • 5 AUGUST, 5.15PM
Charlotte Bray • 14 AUGUST, 5.45PM
Colin Matthews • 16 AUGUST, 5.15PM
Emily Howard • 25 AUGUST, 5.45PM

In addition, Proms Inspire (see 'Nurturing Talent', pages 72–73) brings the freshest young musicians to the Proms, with a concert

Frank Cotrell-Boyce, the writer of the 2012 Olympics Opening Ceremony, gives the BBC Proms Lecture on 16 July

on 15 August of the winning pieces of the Proms Inspire Young Composers' Competition.

PROMS EXTRA FILMS

New to Proms Extra this year is a series of archive documentaries and films featuring legendary artists:

Ahead of a performance of Beethoven's *Missa solemnis*, Myra Hess performs Beethoven's Piano Sonata in A flat major, Op. 110, and Bach (1954)
19 JULY, 4.45PM

Solomon (1956) and Claudio Arrau (1960) in works by Beethoven (Piano Sonatas in F minor, Op. 57, 'Appassionata' and in C minor, Op. 111) and Schubert
24 JULY, 6.00PM

Bernard Haitink at t he Proms with the the BBC Symphony Orchestra (1987), featuring an interview with the conductor
29 JULY, 5.00PM

Paul Tortelier performs excerpts and coaches advanced students in J. S. Bach's Suite No. 3 in C major for solo cello
1 SEPTEMBER, 5.45PM

PROMS SING

With a wealth of choral works at the Proms this year, Mary King and the BBC Singers return with our Proms Sing events. Join them for the chance to explore choral works and sing selected excerpts with professional coaching. You can dabble in operas by Mussorgsky and Rossini, or join in the jazzy melodies of Gershwin. On 17 July there's an opportunity not to be missed – to sing excerpts of Fauré's *Requiem* in the Royal Albert Hall with the Orchestra of the Age of Enlightenment.

Mussorgsky Boris Godunov
16 JULY, 12.30PM–3.30PM

Fauré Requiem
17 JULY, 2.30PM–5.30PM
(Royal Albert Hall)

Tippett A Child of Our Time
23 JULY, 2.00PM–4.00PM

Berlioz Romeo and Juliet
30 JULY, 12.30PM–3.30PM

George and Ira Gershwin Rediscovered
13 AUGUST, 2.00PM–4.00PM

Mozart Mass in C minor
20 AUGUST, 1.00PM–4.00PM

Rossini Semiramide
4 SEPTEMBER, 12.30PM–3.30PM

Suitable for ages 16-plus, except 13 August (suitable for ages 7-plus). Places must be booked in advance. Sign up from 3 June at bbc.co.uk/proms; call 020 7765 0557 or email getinvolved@bbc.co.uk

FAMILY VALUES

If you're thinking of bringing your family to the Proms, here's your guide both to concerts designed especially for families and to an array of free workshops, introductions and masterclasses – so you can choose to listen or to get involved

With over 90 concerts running throughout the summer holidays, the BBC Proms is a great place to introduce your family to some of the world's most celebrated music and musicians. Children aged 7-plus are welcome to all the Proms, which combine world-class performances with a uniquely informal atmosphere, and tickets for under-18s are half-price *(see page 151 for exceptions)*. Plus, with Promming (standing) tickets at £6 always available on the day, a family outing – perhaps combined with a picnic in nearby Hyde Park or a visit to one of the many free national museums in South Kensington – can be spontaneous as well as great value.

If you're not sure where to start, on these pages you'll find a selection of concerts we think families will enjoy. We've also designed a range of free family activities around them, so you can make the most of your visit. From the Ten Pieces II Prom to the return of CBeebies, we've got something to appeal to all ages. You can be moved by your first experience of hearing a symphony orchestra at the Royal Albert Hall, or you can have a go yourself by taking part in a Proms Family Orchestra and Chorus workshop. So, if you're looking for something for the whole family to enjoy this summer, look no further.

Family fun: the CBeebies Prom (2014)

EXPERIENCE A CONCERT

TEN PIECES II PROMS

The BBC Ten Pieces project has introduced millions of primary- and secondary-school children to classical music and encouraged them to get creative with it. The focus in this second year of Ten Pieces is on secondary schools, so this year's Prom will resonate especially with those aged 11-plus, though the whole family is welcome. From Gabriel Prokofiev's Concerto for Turntables and Orchestra to the thrilling second movement of Shostakovich's 10th Symphony, expect a spectacle. The Proms will also feature creative responses and performances from young people across the UK.

Ten Pieces II Proms
PROM 10 • 23 JULY, 11.00AM–1.00PM
PROM 12 • 24 JULY, 4.00PM–6.00PM

For details of free Ten Pieces II family events, see page 71

For more information about the BBC Ten Pieces project, see pages 74–75

CBEEBIES PROMS

Take a journey through time and space with some of your favourite CBeebies characters and the BBC Concert Orchestra. With adventures to have and worlds to explore, who knows what will be found in the Royal Albert Hall: dinosaurs, pirates, planets and stars … along with CBeebies musical favourites and orchestral classics from the BBC Concert Orchestra. These hour-long concerts are aimed at 0- to 5-year-olds and their families.

CBeebies Proms
PROM 56 • 28 AUGUST, 11.00AM–12.00PM
PROM 58 • 29 AUGUST, 11.00AM–12.00PM

OUR FAMILY SELECTION

Here's our selection of matinee and evening Proms to get your family started.

These concerts offer a great opportunity for a family day out. Each one is accompanied by a **Proms Family** workshop or a **Proms Family Orchestra and Chorus** event (*see page 71*).

Ravel's 'Boléro
PROM 4 • 18
Proms Family wor

Ten Pieces II
PROM 12 • 24
Proms Family Orch

Prokofiev's 'Romeo and Juliet'
PROM 16 • 27 JULY, 7.00PM
Proms Family workshop 5.15pm–6.00pm

Mozart from Memory
PROM 21 • 31 JULY, 3.45PM
Proms Family Orchestra and Chorus 11.00am–1.00pm

Schubert's Ninth
PROM 24 • 2 AUGUST, 7.30PM
Proms Family workshop 5.45pm–6.30pm

Stravinsky's 'The Firebird'
PROM 30 • 7 AUGUST, 3.45PM
Proms Family workshop 2.00pm–2.45pm

George and Ira Gershwin Rediscovered
PROM 38 • 13 AUGUST, 7.00PM
Proms Family Orchestra and Chorus 11.00am–1.00pm
Proms Sing 2.00pm–4.00pm

Tchaikovsky's Fifth
PROM 47 • 21 AUGUST, 3.45PM
Proms Family workshop 2.00pm–2.45pm

CBeebies Proms
PROMS 56 & 58 • 28 & 29 AUGUST, 11.00AM
Family events 12.30pm–2.30pm

Dudamel and the Simón Bolívar Symphony Orchestra
PROM 67 • 4 SEPTEMBER, 3.45PM
Proms Family workshop 2.00pm–2.45pm

All family events are free but tickets must be bought for concerts. For full concert listings, see pages 111–149. For booking information, see pages 150–157.

'BELIEVE THE HYPE'

NEW YORK POST

ROALD DAHL'S

Matilda

THE MUSICAL

MatildaTheMusical.com
CAMBRIDGE THEATRE, London, WC2H 9HU

GET INVOLVED

PROMS FAMILY WORKSHOPS

Proms Family workshops are free interactive sessions aimed at providing a perfect introduction to the pieces you'll hear in the following concert. Professional musicians bring the music to life and, if you have an instrument of your own, bring it along and make some noise! Suitable for anyone aged 7-plus, and all musical abilities. Free family-friendly programme notes are also provided.

All Proms Family workshops take place at Imperial College Union, see page 160 for details). No booking is necessary. Entry is on a first-come first-served basis (doors open 30 minutes before the event begins; capacity is limited). Events end one hour before the following Proms concert.

PROMS FAMILY ORCHESTRA AND CHORUS – AND PROMS SING

The **Proms Family Orchestra and Chorus** workshops introduce families to making music together. Whether you're a complete novice or an aspiring virtuoso, the whole family can join in. You'll form part of a full-sized orchestra and chorus, led by professional musicians and inspired by the music of the related Prom that day. This year's Family Orchestra events take inspiration from Ten Pieces II (24 July), Richard Strauss and Mozart (31 July) and George and Ira Gershwin (13 August). As with our Proms Family workshops, these events are designed to enhance your family's concert experience, but you can still sign up if you haven't got concert tickets. Open to all levels of ability and experience (ages 7-plus). You don't need to be able to read music. Non-instrumentalists can join the chorus and percussion section.

Group support: Proms Family Orchestra

This year's **Proms Sing** events feature a special family event with the BBC Singers celebrating George and Ira Gershwin (13 August). You'll have the chance to discover some new works as well as lending your voice to old favourites, in a friendly environment. Open to all levels of ability and experience (ages 7-plus). You don't need to be able to read music. (*See page 69 for dates and times.*)

CBEEBIES FAMILY EVENTS

Continue your CBeebies family adventure at the Proms and join in our range of activities from arts and crafts to music and dance. You never know, your favourite CBeebies character might even pop in to say hello! Suitable for all ages.

All family events take place at Imperial College Union (see page 160 for details.) Places must be booked in advance. Sign up from 3 June at bbc.co.uk/proms, call 020 7765 0557 or email getinvolved@bbc.co.uk.

Get Playing with BBC Music (from June)
Whatever level you are, we want to inspire people across the UK to pick up an instrument and 'Get Playing'. Keep watching the Get Playing website to find out how you can be involved in the Last Night of the Proms celebrations: bbc.co.uk/getplaying #BBCGetplaying

NURTURING TALENT

With a host of the UK's talented youth orchestras and choirs appearing this summer – as well as opportunities for young composers – **Warwick Thompson** looks at some of the myriad ways in which the Proms nurtures young talent

'The bottom line is that, without the Proms Inspire composing competition, I wouldn't now be a composer. For that I'm eternally grateful,' says Tom Harrold, whose piece *Raze* will receive its world premiere at this year's Last Night of the Proms, performed jointly by members of the BBC Symphony Orchestra and the Proms Youth Ensemble. Harrold is far from being the only musician to feel gratitude for the impact which the talent-nurturing aspect of the festival has had on his career and, as the Proms's seed-sowing tradition continues more energetically than ever this year, there are likely to be hundreds more joining him. BBC Proms Inspire; Ten Pieces; Proms Sessions; Proms Youth Ensemble; Proms Youth Choir; this year's Proms youth weekend; Family events; not to mention BBC schemes such as BBC Young Musician, Radio 3's New Generation Artists and BBC Music Introducing. The points of access for budding players, performers and composers are almost too many to mention.

They overlap in a fascinating kaleidoscope of opportunity too. Take the Proms Youth Choir's performance of Verdi's *Requiem* (Prom 74), which also just happens to be one of the works included in the brilliant Ten Pieces scheme *(see pages 74–75)*, offering secondary-school children the chance to create musical and visual responses to a selection of 10 classical pieces: the chorus will include a choir made up of young singers from across the UK who have come through the Ten Pieces scheme. The overlaps go on and on, and ensure that the nurturing aspect of the Proms is at the very heart of the season: no sidelining or box-ticking here.

Indeed, the exposure which the Last Night offers a young composer is one of the most exciting elements of the whole experience for Tom Harrold, who says that *Raze* will be a 'noisy, carnival-like piece which will soar and hurtle to its climax'. He goes on: 'Proms Inspire is simply the best platform to get young musicians' music performed, broadcast and heard by

Saron Jeynes/BBC

an audience. Before I entered the Proms competition, I was very much focusing on being a pianist, and I didn't take composing too seriously. But being a winner really changed everything, and showed me how I could grow and develop. The exposure was excellent.'

In addition to the Proms's own two youth ensembles, many other young musicians will be descending on the Royal Albert Hall during a youth-themed weekend (Proms 28–30). The National Youth Jazz Orchestra of Scotland plays Duke Ellington's *Such Sweet Thunder*; the National Youth Orchestra of Great Britain plays Strauss's *Also sprach Zarathustra* and Holst's *The Planets*; and the National Youth Orchestra of Scotland plays Stravinsky's *The Firebird*, and Tchaikovsky's Piano Concerto No. 2 with Pavel Kolesnikov as soloist.

No doubt the many young performers will have a chance to meet up and swap stories during the weekend. For Simon Halsey, Director of the Proms Youth Choir, this is one of the most exciting aspects of his job: 'It's so pleasing to see the burgeoning friendships and the knock-on effects afterwards.' He's also thrilled that the Proms offers young musicians a chance to perform in repertoire to which they don't regularly have access. 'At a younger age you usually sing in smaller groups, often without accompaniment. But I feel strongly that the future of our great symphony choruses depends on giving young people a taste for this repertoire and for working in a large group.'

For Ellara Wakely, Senior Learning Manager at the Proms, seeing young performers play alongside established professionals (and seeing young hopefuls learn from and chat to professionals in the Proms Sessions events) is one of the happiest parts of her work. 'There

have been so many occasions when it feels like you can see the young participants having a light-bulb moment. I'll never forget the first rehearsal of the Proms Youth Ensemble with Nicholas Collon and Aurora Orchestra last year, when they played Anna Meredith's *Smatter Hauler* from memory for the first time. The piece had been specially written for the ensemble, who had never met before, and the first play-through was nerve-racking. But once we heard them we knew there was nothing to worry about. It's great to keep pushing at the boundaries of what an ensemble can do.' It's unlikely there will be too many worries on that score this year. ●

Warwick Thompson is the London opera and theatre critic for BlouinArtInfo.com, and also regularly writes for Opera, Opera Now, Gramophone, *the Royal Opera, Covent Garden and Glyndebourne.*

More opportunities for young musicians at the Proms

The **Proms Inspire Young Composers' Competition** is open to 12- to 18-year-olds (closing date for entries 26 May). There are also two types of **BBC Proms Sessions**: for young composers, held during the season with some of the leading composers featured in the season; and – in partnership with Royal Albert Hall Education & Outreach – for young musicians, who have the chance to work with cellist Guy Johnston, jazz singer-songwriter Jamie Cullum and DJ Mr Switch, among others. Booking opens 3 June. To become a Proms Young Composer or sign up for these events, contact Proms Learning at getinvolved@bbc.co.uk, or phone 020 7765 5575.

Proms Extra Lates offer the chance to hear emerging world, jazz and folk musicians perform in the Royal Albert Hall's Elgar Room, alongside upcoming poets selected in collaboration with the Poetry Society. Proms Extra Lates are free events but tickets must be booked in advance unless you have attended that evening's Prom: for more details, visit the Royal Albert Hall website: www.royalalberthall.com.

The **Proms Poetry Competition** returns this year with entries in two categories (ages 12–18 and over-19). Winners are announced at the Proms Extra event on 8 September. The competition is launched on 10 June: for more details, visit *The Verb* page on the Radio 3 website – bbc.co.uk/radio3.

Trumpeters of the National Youth Orchestra of Great Britain performing in Berlin's Gendarmentmarkt prior to a concert at the Young Euro Classic festival last year

National Youth Choir of Scotland
PROM 20 • 30 JULY

National Youth Jazz Orchestra of Scotland
PROM 28 • 5 AUGUST

City of Birmingham Symphony Youth Chorus (women's voices), National Youth Orchestra of Great Britain
PROM 29 • 6 AUGUST

National Youth Orchestra of Scotland
PROM 30 • 7 AUGUST

Proms Youth Choir
PROM 74 • 9 SEPTEMBER

Proms Youth Ensemble
PROM 75 • 10 SEPTEMBER

TEN PIECES II

Andrew Stewart goes on the trail of the BBC scheme to get classical music into schools – which, in its second year, turns its focus from primary schools to secondary

Ten Pieces offers schools a substantial resource for introducing classical music to all. Launched in 2014 by a new partnership between BBC Learning, BBC Music and the BBC Performing Groups, the initiative is about seed-planting, the idea being to cultivate lifelong creativity and invention. Indeed, the project's greatest fruits are likely to be reaped over time, as children develop and mature with classical music as part of their everyday lives.

Ten Pieces arose as a primary-schools project and has now branched out to reach secondary pupils. Its common entry point is provided by a high-octane BBC film screened in cinemas, on television and freely available online. Ten Pieces II, smartly designed for teenagers, aired on BBC Two on Boxing Day and on CBBC the following weekend. Its choice of works spans everything from Haydn's Trumpet Concerto and Vaughan Williams's *The Lark Ascending* to works by living composers, such as Gabriel Prokofiev's Concerto for Turntables and Orchestra and Anna Clyne's *Night Ferry*. Former music student James May, singer-songwriter Pixie Lott, actor Christopher Ecclestone, Radio 1's Clara Amfo and footballer-turned-broadcaster Dion Dublin are among the film's presenters, while Ten Pieces Ambassadors Alison Balsom, Nicola Benedetti and DJ Mr Switch appear as soloists with the BBC Philharmonic and rising-star conductor Alpesh Chauhan.

Nicola Benedetti notes how each piece is selected for its ability to engage young minds and ignite fresh ideas. The violinist, herself a tireless advocate of music education, points to the creative responses uploaded to the project's website, the best of which are presented during this year's Ten Pieces II Proms on Saturday 23 and Sunday 24 July. 'Of course, there are thousands of pieces of classical music, which is precisely what can make it so overwhelming and daunting,' notes Benedetti. 'I think curation is half the battle in getting people started with classical music.'

Heidi Nixon, a Music Education Leader with Worcestershire Youth Music, recalls hearing a group of 8-year-olds singing the opening of Beethoven's Fifth Symphony after the primary-school cinema screenings. She was also moved by seeing many primary teachers explore classical music for the first time. Nixon belongs to a nationwide network of around

It has inspired me to create my own music – it's not as hard as I thought it would be.

Ten Pieces secondary participant

260 Ten Pieces Champions drawn from music hubs, music-education services and arts organisations. Their enthusiasm and expertise have helped turn each of the 10 pieces into catalysts for children's creative work.

'I believe Ten Pieces has filled a void,' Nixon observes. The Key Stage 2 pupils she worked with last year, she continues, were instantly hooked by the energy and commitment of the BBC National Orchestra of Wales on film. 'Young people can make up their minds about whether they like classical works or not. But they have to hear them first. It's not good enough simply to ignore classical music at school.'

For Benedetti, the idea that a child might go through school without experiencing classical music is a cause for concern. 'It has always stumped me that, if a piece of music is not instantly adored and seen as fun, it's dismissed by adults as boring for kids,' she says. The Ten Pieces films, she adds, may be bite-sized and vibrant but they encourage much more than superficial excitement, inviting reflection, concentration and intense listening. 'That's the reason to show them to everyone. The most ingenious ideas are often the simplest, and this one really is excellent.'

Before he embarked on his career as a baritone and composer Roderick Williams worked for three years as a school music teacher. A Ten Pieces Ambassador, he wishes the project had been available during his time in the classroom. 'It's a very powerful and impressive resource. The BBC has invested a lot of effort and talent into the Ten Pieces films, making something that's ideal for cinemas and for showing in school. With production values that we're used to seeing in *Doctor Who* and *Sherlock*, it can wow young people in a way that watching something on a small screen simply cannot do. And people love the fact that it's an interactive project, allowing children to upload their artistic responses to the Ten Pieces website. It's a great way to get young people engaged with music.'

Classical music and young people have already forged a strong union at Sistema Scotland's showcase project with children from deprived communities in Stirling. Peter Nicholson, Team Leader at the Big Noise Raploch and a Ten Pieces Champion, says that the BBC's initiative has opened doors to new Big Noise performing partnerships with local schools. 'Ten Pieces II is saying to a difficult teenage audience that classical music

DJ Mr Switch, who hits the decks in Gabriel Prokofiev's Concerto for Turntables and Orchestra at the Ten Pieces II Proms: he also appears in one of a series of video tutorials on the Ten Pieces website

is not something "other", that it can be part of your daily diet. The online resource is terrific. Ten Pieces helps widen the pathways to classical music and raise our children's aspirations. It has provided a framework, a forum and a context for bringing our kids together with other young musicians.' ●

Andrew Stewart is a freelance music journalist and writer. He has contributed articles to newspapers and periodicals including *BBC Music Magazine*, *Classical Music*, *Music Week* and the *Independent on Sunday*, and created programme notes for a wide range of classical record labels, orchestras and concert halls.

Watch the Ten Pieces II film, introducing each of the chosen works, at bbc.co.uk/tenpieces

Ten Pieces II Proms

Featuring all Ten Pieces, plus children's creative responses to the works

PROMS 10 & 12

SATURDAY 23 JULY • 11.00AM
SUNDAY 24 JULY • 4.00PM

SONIC STRUCTURES

The parallels between music and the spaces in which it is performed were drawn long before Goethe's description of architecture as 'frozen music'. As the Proms ventures out to four venues across London this year, **Igor Toronyi-Lalic** considers how buildings continue to shape our musical experiences, in conversation with the architect **Daniel Libeskind**

House-swapping is not quite as revolutionary a fad in music as some might like to think. Classical music has never been spatially faithful. Architectural promiscuity is one of its oldest traditions – and its marriage to the concert hall a pretty recent fix.

The first London Contemporary Music Festival in 2013 was held at a multi-storey car park in Peckham (one of four venues where the Proms heads this summer for the 'Proms at …' series). When I, as co-director of the festival, suggested to the experimentalist composer Charlemagne Palestine that he was probably quite excited to be performing in a municipal car park, he laughed. 'This will be my sixth concert in a car park!' His first was in the 1960s.

The Proms expands this year's festival with a wider programme of site-specific performances – Rossini's *Petite messe solennelle* at the Chapel of the Old Royal Naval College in Greenwich and music by Steve Reich in the car park at Peckham. Seventeenth-century incidental music for Shakespeare's plays will be performed in the candlelit intimacy of the Jacobean-style Sam Wanamaker Playhouse and, 45 years after Pierre Boulez spearheaded the Proms' first forays to the Roundhouse, the concerts revisit the iconic engine shed turned pioneering arts centre in Camden Town.

It makes sense that architecture is being considered. Architecture is music. It shapes it. It guides it. It often determines it formally. We only get the music our buildings allow us to have. As opera houses got bigger, so did the voices. As architecture and society became more domestic, so too did music. The myriad ways in which composers have worked with sound in the 20th and 21st centuries have often been about tailoring musical expression to space.

Most striking is the example of Edgard Varèse's *Poème électronique*, composed for the Philips Pavilion at the 1958 World Fair. Diffused through numerous speakers, the piece ricocheted around the structure's swooping Futuristic curves. The Pavilion itself was

The myriad ways in which composers have worked with sound have often been about tailoring musical expression to space.

conceived under the influence of musical ideas, engineer and composer Iannis Xenakis (Le Corbusier's assistant on the project) drawing on compositional techniques such as *glissandos* to realise the Pavilion's hyperbolic parabolas.

Elsewhere, in the Jeita caves of Lebanon, in 1969, Stockhausen allowed his minimalist vocal piece *Stimmung* to bounce off the stalactites, among which 180 loudspeakers were planted. In Chicago in 1967, in an arena for auctioning livestock, John Cage premiered his opera *Musicircus*, the seated rim acting as a stage and the arena as the auditorium. Aircraft hangars, swimming pools, bunkers, helicopters: there are few places today where classical music hasn't gone.

This May, in Frankfurt, things are being taken one step further. Marin Marais's *Tableau de l'opération de la taille* ('Description of a Bladder-Stone Operation') for viola da gamba and harpsichord will be performed in an operating theatre. Down the road a fire

training centre will resound to Biber and Beethoven (transcribed by Liszt), a project that is the brainchild of musician-cum-architect Daniel Libeskind working with the Alte Oper. For him, the river flows only one way: without music, there would be no architecture. 'Architecture is an extension of music, not the other way round,' he insists. Libeskind means this quite literally. His Jewish Museum in Berlin is first and foremost a building. But it is also a realisation of Schoenberg's opera *Moses und Aron*. 'I treated the void at the centre of the museum as an acoustical space,' he explains. He then applied his analysis of Schoenberg's score to the plans. The reverberations of the footsteps of museum visitors became a completion of the opera. Every building he's ever designed has been conceived acoustically.

Window cuts (deriving from a dislocated Star of David) in the zinc facade of the Jewish Museum in Berlin – which Daniel Libeskind designed as a realisation of Schoenberg's opera *Moses und Aron*

Michele Nastasi

A membership club
with a difference

ROSL is a unique not-for-profit, private members organisation; bringing people together from around the world to meet, socialise and foster an interest in the Commonwealth. This is best realised through our Arts programme that works with young classical musicians and visual artists, and our humanitarian programme of education and enterprise projects. Our Members make a difference to people's lives while enjoying the comforts of clubhouses in Edinburgh and London.

To find out more about becoming a member, or attending our exceptional programme of concerts, exhibitions and book events visit **www.rosl.org.uk** or call **020 7408 0214**.

London
Over-Seas House
Park Place
St James's Street
London SW1A 1LR

Edinburgh
Over-Seas House
100 Princes Street
Edinburgh EH2 3AB

ROSL
ROYAL OVER-SEAS LEAGUE

The Philips Pavilion, designed by Le Corbusier and Xenakis for the 1958 World Fair in Brussels – its cavernous acoustic was created by asbestos-coated walls

....

'Our sense of balance is located, as we know, in our ear not in the eye,' he explains. 'So the acoustic cannot just be an added extra. Every building is a musical instrument.' Libeskind even likes to play his architectural mock-ups. 'I often examine my wood-and-cardboard models by knocking them … Different bits of a building sound differently.'

Libeskind's first great love was music. Accordion was his instrument. 'It was almost as big as my body when I began playing.' He won prizes (including one shared with Itzhak Perlman), played on the first TV broadcast in Poland and stormed New York with his virtuosic transcriptions. 'I made more

money than I do now!' He got so good Isaac Stern told him he had exhausted the possibilities of the instrument and that it was now time for him to switch to piano. He disobeyed and took up drawing instead. But he never gave up music, he says: 'I just changed my instrument.'

Libeskind is not alone, he insists. All the architects whose work he loves – whether it's Bramante or Alberti or those who built the Gothic cathedrals – were people who loved music. 'They saw music and architecture as intertwined.' The parallels are practical as well as conceptual. When he master-plans a building, he feels he is 'conducting a score – and, just as the conductor usually has his back to the audience, so a master-planner is never visible.'

Conversely, many of the composers Libeskind loves he sees as architects. 'Bach is probably the best architect in the world,' he says, 'because he constructed spaces that are thoroughly architectural. And encoded in these massive works are his own personal, mystical ideas.'

Has Libeskind ever wanted to build a concert hall? 'I entered a competition for one that I lost because I wanted to let light into the auditorium.' Why does he think this tradition continues? 'It's a hang-over from the past,' he thinks, 'a tradition that people have not re-examined. But we should be able to expose music to the forces of everyday life – the magic force is light.' Would he put his hat into the ring for the new concert hall proposed for London? 'I'd love to!'

Sending carefully constructed music out into the acoustic wilds of a car park in the name of experimentation will irritate some. But this is not experimentation for the sake of experimentation. Forcing musicians to wrestle

with their acoustic surroundings, to beat the sound into shape, encourages more careful listening and often a more lively performance. It's good to challenge music, says Libeskind.

'[In Frankfurt] I have a solo violinist performing the works of Paganini in an arena that holds 50,000 people,' says Libeskind. 'That's the kind of virtuosity Paganini was into!'

To allow music to have the best acoustic is to permit it to rest on its laurels. 'You can play a perfect Steinway and play all the right notes and it will not move anybody,' Libeskind says. 'And you can play an arguably lesser piano, as Sviatoslav Richter did in some of those concerts across Siberia in the 1980s, and those performances will never be forgotten.'

'The gentrification of music is not right,' he explains. 'To play in circumstances which are almost impossible is what makes music come alive … And, as Horowitz once said, perfection in music is itself a form of imperfection.' ●

Igor Toronyi-Lalic is arts editor at *The Spectator*, author of *Benjamin Britten* (Penguin, 2013) and co-director of the London Contemporary Music Festival.

PROMS AT … THE CHAPEL, OLD ROYAL NAVAL COLLEGE • 6 AUGUST

PROMS AT … SAM WANAMAKER PLAYHOUSE • 13 AUGUST

PROMS AT … ROUNDHOUSE, CAMDEN • 20 AUGUST

PROMS AT … BOLD TENDENCIES, PECKHAM • 3 SEPTEMBER

1 thing that matters is protecting your passion

Protect what matters to you with Allianz Musical Insurance, the UK's No.1 specialist instrument insurer.

- Instrument & accessory cover
- Unlimited professional use
- Accidental damage & theft
- Premiums from £33 per year

Get a quote:

 allianzmusic.co.uk

 0330 100 9624

We're proud to work with some of the UK's leading orchestras, including Bournemouth Symphony Orchestra
BSOlive.com

Allianz ⑪

#MyMusicMatters

Terms and conditions apply. Allianz Musical Insurance is a trading name of Allianz Insurance plc.

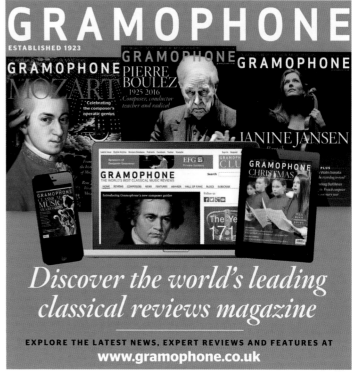

MY PROMS
MAX RICHTER
composer

Erik Weiss

I started going to the Proms as a student. Every year, when the Guide was published, we would go through it, circling our top 20 or so concerts and then queue all day to get places in the Arena (back in the days of student grants, we could afford to go to that many). This became a sort of ritual and an invaluable introduction to all sorts of music I hadn't had the chance to hear live before.

There have been so many special nights that it's tricky to pick out single events to mention – in fact, one of the hallmarks of the Proms is that it presents a series of exceptional concerts all bunched together – but a few do stick in my mind. Like many student composers, I was obsessed by the music of Mahler, and I strongly recall a wonderful Ninth Symphony conducted by Andrew Davis in 1986. It's a demanding work for both performers and audiences, and you could have heard a pin drop throughout. Near the end we spotted Bernard Haitink in the audience.

> ❝ The Proms is a series of exceptional concerts all bunched together. ❞

Roger Woodward's 1988 recital at Kensington Town Hall was also memorable. This was the first time I'd heard the fascinating Barraqué Piano Sonata live, and Woodward's performances of Stockhausen's *Klavierstücke IX* and *XI* were typically accomplished.

The 1991 concert featuring Xenakis's *Shaar* is another landmark. Verdi's *Requiem* from 2001, with the Chorus of the Teatro Comunale di Bologna, was another amazing night. Hearing the music sung by that choir, I felt like I 'got' Verdi for the first time. ●

Favourite composer: Purcell – his fusion of brilliant technique and emotional intensity is wonderful and his harmonic language is thrilling.

Most recent musical 'discovery': The architecture of Sibelius's later symphonic works, the guitar tones on records by the band Low, the textures in Tyondai Braxton's *Hive*, the piano-playing of Craig Taborn …

Proms 2016 highlight: Prom 46 – this includes the UK premiere (finally!) of Gérard Grisey's *Dérives*, with the added bonus for me of Mahler's *Rückert-Lieder*.

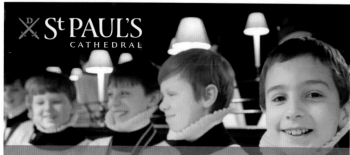

MY PROMS
LAURA MVULA
singer-songwriter

I never actually went to the BBC Proms when I was younger but I was part of a Schools Prom at the Royal Albert Hall way back in the early 2000s, when I was playing in school orchestras. I remember feeling in awe of the massiveness of the room, and balloons falling from the ceiling! I never imagined that I'd be there in my own right later.

The first Prom at which I performed – the Urban Classic Prom in 2013 – came about through the conductor Jules Buckley, who said they were going to remix my songs with orchestra. Jules sent me an arrangement he'd done of one of the songs and it made instant sense to me that this was something I should jump at. My music fitted so well with the occasion and the whole concert felt like coming home. It felt like, 'Oh, so this is how it's supposed to sound!'

We started talking about my own Prom, which I thought was a joke at first! I thought people who were expecting an orchestral show might think, what is

It was so quiet and still – you don't expect that sense of stillness. 99

this girl doing, or the other way round, so I just didn't know if people would come. But working with Jules again on my Late Night Prom in 2014 was pretty special. It felt like a wedding day. I'll never forget walking out and looking up at the audience. It felt like I had entered a dream where the RAH was my bedroom, and everyone was there, and it was so quiet and still. There are so many people in the Hall that you don't expect that sense of stillness; certainly not a prolonged silence. It was a magical, serene moment. Another special moment was starting the Michael Jackson song 'Human Nature', which was just myself, with my brother accompanying on cello. It was pin-drop silence. ●

Favourite composer: Debussy. I played the Arabesque No. 1 in a piano lesson and my teacher said he thought I had a thing for French music, for Impressionism. I used to get terrible insomnia, and Debussy's String Quartet would always send me to sleep – in the best way!

Most recent musical 'discovery': Actually, I didn't expect my own album to be as progressive as it is. This time I've been influenced by Afro-beat and Fela Kuti, and a lot of more hard-rock, punkish noises.

Proms 2016 highlight: Quincy Jones (Prom 49), without a shadow of a doubt! It's a perfect fit with the Metropole Orkest. I know it'll be a magical concert.

NEW MUSIC

Ed McKeon previews the diverse mix of world, UK and London premieres at this year's Proms

Ed McKeon is Director of Third Ear Music and Artistic Director of the British Composer Awards. He is also a lecturer, researcher and occasional broadcaster, specialising in the production of new music.

HANS ABRAHAMSEN

(BORN 1952)

let me tell you (2013)
London premiere

PROM 55 • 27 AUGUST

Hans Abrahamsen is meticulous, twice pausing in his career to reassess, before each time returning to composing, with a renewed clarity of sound. His music is direct and has a beguiling simplicity, often reaching for the upper registers, 'like singing in the sky', an apt description of Barbara Hannigan's voice. This new work sets texts from writer and music critic Paul Griffiths's novel *let me tell you*, itself a reworking of the speech that Shakespeare breathes into Ophelia in *Hamlet*, a musical treatment that limits itself to variations on her 481-word vocabulary: 'What is music, if not time?' she sings. Abrahamsen likewise spins a diaphanous texture from greatly simplified materials.

Winning both a 2015 Royal Philharmonic Society Award and the 2016 Grawemeyer Award, the work has been praised for both its string writing and its silvery vocal lines. For this, Abrahamsen's first true vocal piece, Hannigan has been muse as well as oracle, having proposed to the Berlin Philharmonic that it commission the work.

'I have the feeling that in this piece I have made something which is perhaps more open but still full of mystery, and, for me, what I'm searching for,' Abrahamsen says. 'When I did the piece, I felt that everything came into its right place.'

THOMAS ADÈS

(BORN 1971)

Lieux retrouvés (2009, arr. 2015)
*world premiere of version
with orchestra*

PROM 40 • 15 AUGUST

Thomas Adès's music has often featured at the Proms, although this familiarity is offset by its sly deviations, 'as if the world of conventional tonal progressions and processes were shifted by a knight's move', in Tom Service's memorable phrase. With this music, nothing is quite as it seems.

The four movements of Adès's 'Rediscovered Places' hint at programmes, but these are insistently musical impressions. In 'Les eaux', 'the movement of the waters is recreated in flexible fluid counterpoint, which eddies and flows according to how each line responds to the other current,' Adès explains. 'La montagne' – in 'Tempo di promenade' – appears to trace a hard-working ascent, which is achieved through a precipitous logic of melodic canons. A meditative air stills the slow movement of 'Les champs', only to vanish mid-thought; while 'La ville', a 'cancan macabre' inspired in part by Liszt's late *Csárdás macabre*, draws the work to a close with off-kilter Offenbach and an insouciant Trio in a high register.

Originally written for cello and piano, *Lieux retrouvés* is here presented in a new version for cello and orchestra. As ever, Adès creates highly polished music in which the instruments glide with expert care. Only we are cautioned to avoid slipping on its deceptive surfaces, to listen with steady ears.

JULIAN ANDERSON

(BORN 1967)

Incantesimi (2015–16)
UK premiere

PROM 66 • 3 SEPTEMBER

Invited by Sir Simon Rattle to write for the Berlin Philharmonic, Julian Anderson avoided the rush to blaze a trail, fast and loud. 'I hear a special quality in the way the orchestra colours slow music,' he explains. 'I also think Rattle has a wonderful way of carrying and characterising long lines. There's rhythm and flow. So I decided to write something showing that off.'

Since writing *The Discovery of Heaven* (2011), which moved between the sacred and profane, Anderson had wanted to create a piece focusing only on the spiritual. 'I'm not conventionally religious, but I am interested in spiritual matters. In our everyday world, these are often missing or marginalised,' he says.

Anderson is working with five musical ideas that orbit around each other 'in ever differing relationships, somewhat like planets in an orrery [a model of celestial bodies in motion]'. Among them is a recurring solo for cor anglais, an instrument for which Anderson has special affection.

'Music can enable people to experience different kinds of time,' he suggests, comparing his work to a TARDIS: 'It's an eight-minute span of time on the outside, but the inside – the musical substance – gives a sense of being much more expansive, which is an illusion only music can give.'

LERA AUERBACH

(BORN 1973)

The Infant Minstrel and His Peculiar Menagerie (2016)
BBC co-commission with the Bergen Philharmonic and the Orchestre de la Suisse Romande: UK premiere

PROM 22 • 31 JULY

Lera Auerbach's latest work, *The Infant Minstrel and His Peculiar Menagerie*, speaks to the young and the young at heart. Along the way, we meet characters such as the Common Corporant, the Moon Rider and a Flying Pig that enjoys sitting on a cloud watching the crowd. She places it in the tradition of 'nonsense' authors from Edward Lear and Mother Goose to Shel Silverstein and Tim Burton, as 'child-like, yet enigmatic and humorous'.

This prolific composer, poet, visual artist and concert pianist – who defected from Russia to the USA in 1991 while on a concert tour, at the age of 17 – is also a Cultural Leader for the World Economic Forum, speaking on borderless creativity. Driven and on a mission, she is often drawn to texts, both her own and the poetry of others, notably Alexander Blok and Marina Tsvetaeva. Her interest in the fabulous and the young is reflected in such works as her ballet *The Little Mermaid*.

For her Proms debut, this symphonic fantasy for solo violin, choir and orchestra presents violinist Vadim Gluzman in the role of a travelling musical storyteller who introduces a collection of wondrous tales, guiding listeners through a voyage of the imagination.

SALLY BEAMISH

(BORN 1956)

Merula perpetua (2016)
BBC co-commission with the Royal Philharmonic Society: world premiere

PCM 7 • 29 AUGUST

'Merula' is the Latin for blackbird, the national bird of Sweden, where Sally Beamish's music has long been championed for its sweet melodies and sympathetic resonances. Here, though, she relates a story of a particular bird, whose 'plaintive, grief-ridden, obsessive' song rang day and night by her window, its apparent nocturnal disorientation sweetly disturbing her own sleep on arrival in Glasgow after 20 years in rural Stirlingshire.

An accomplished storyteller, both in person and through her music, Beamish's work gives a vivid and engaging account of her roots, including her interests in Scottish music, jazz, and the concerto form.

The daughter of violinist Ursula Snow, Beamish took up the viola and played it for many years, but abandoned it after the theft of a beloved instrument in 1989. Her own daughter, Stephanie, is now a luthier, and made as her first instrument a viola for Sally herself.

'Starting to play again,' Sally says, 'I realised how much I had missed performing. The blackbird sang as I rediscovered the joy of playing and this work expresses that journey, through the blackbird's song.'

MICHAEL BERKELEY

(BORN 1948)

Violin Concerto (2016)
BBC commission: world premiere

PROM 16 • 27 JULY

The concerto form clearly fascinates Michael Berkeley: this new work will be his ninth. 'I've always been interested in the friction and synthesis between soloist and orchestra and wanted to write a violin concerto for some time,' he explains.

Well-known also for presenting BBC Radio 3's *Private Passions*, his broadcast work has introduced him — and us — to a wide variety of musicians and artists, which also contributes to this new work in the form of *bols*, the 'spoken rhythm' of tabla players in Indian music. 'I interviewed the choreographer Akram Khan and was struck by this music when I saw one of his productions.'

This concerto follows a difficult period in Berkeley's life — after he suffered hearing loss in 2010 and, more recently, his wife's sudden and untimely death. Deborah Rogers was much-loved and admired, becoming the first literary agent to receive the London Book Fair lifetime achievement award — from one of her authors, Kazuo Ishiguro — in 2014, just weeks before she died. Written as a single movement, so the emotional arc and tension remain unbroken, the Violin Concerto is composed in her memory. Berkeley describes the feelings he wants to capture: 'It deals with both grief and celebration. More than that, though, is the turbulence and rage that come with loss.'

CHARLOTTE BRAY

(BORN 1982)

Falling in the Fire (2015)
BBC commission: world premiere

PROM 39 • 14 AUGUST

On the day she settled down to write this cello concerto, Charlotte Bray found herself appalled by and captive to the news of the destruction of the ancient city of Palmyra by the so-called Islamic State. Her plans for the work went to ruin and she busied herself researching — rebuilding the city, its culture, history and monuments in her imagination. 'The razing of the temples provided an inception for the work, the emerging humanitarian crises formed its body. I felt an overwhelming need to situate the work in these real events.'

Inspired by the work of the investigative photo-journalist Tim Hetherington, who was killed by shrapnel in Libya in 2011, the piece began to take shape. The cognitive dissonance between the experience of war and of 'everyday' reality, two incompatible yet neighbouring zones of experience, gave Bray her structural idea. Between sections of intense striving and numbed contemplation, shadowed paths are cast by 'slow, eerie interludes that suspend time and pulse, using sounds like the low humming of a nearby helicopter or the intense high ringing "heard" after an explosion.'

Amid this wreckage of sense, Bray seems to ask, which is more 'real': the apparently stable sections, or these unresolved bridges that span the gulf?

FRANCISCO COLL

(BORN 1985)

Four Iberian Miniatures (2014)
London premiere

PROM 40 • 15 AUGUST

The Spanish composer Francisco Coll showed early talent as a painter as well as on trombone, before focusing on composition, first in Valencia and Madrid, then with Thomas Adès. Artworks continue to inspire his music, notably those by the Surrealists and Neo-Expressionists. So, while the *Four Iberian Miniatures* are not representations of galleried scenes, they are nevertheless 'painterly' treatments of 'Spanish' themes — in the spirit, perhaps, of Dalí and Buñuel, where time melts and shadows form at midnight.

'As a child, I played in an amateur wind band, where most of the repertoire was folkloric music, especially pasodobles,' he recalls. This 'two-step' of the bullring is doubled by the sudden sidesteps we hear between dancing violin melodies and the un-limbed torsos of spectral harmonies.

Originally written for piano and violin, this elaboration and orchestration of the *Four Iberian Miniatures* adds flecks of colour and bolder strokes. At times the ensemble fizzes and sparks like the embers of a campfire, at others its dreams wrestle with whispery apparitions. 'I find Spanish popular music a very rich source to incorporate in my own musical landscape,' he enthuses. 'In some way I was filtering flamenco music through my own musical language.'

PAUL DESENNE

(BORN 1959)

Hipnosis mariposa (2014)
UK premiere

PROM 67 • 4 SEPTEMBER

Born in Caracas to French and American parents, Paul Desenne combines influences from the Renaissance to the present day with the popular and folk traditions of Latin American music.

As a cellist, he was a founding member of the Simón Bolívar Youth Orchestra in 1977 and, following advanced studies in Paris, returned to Venezuela, also becoming a columnist for *El Nacional* (the national newspaper), publishing and broadcasting satirical essays and programmes.

Hipnosis mariposa was written as a homage to Simón Díaz, one of Venezuela's most renowned popular composers. Taking his song 'El becerrito' (The Little Calf), known to children throughout the country, Desenne weaves its melody into an 'orchestral reverie', drawing in particular on the playfulness of its traditional 5/8 rhythms.

Like Saint-Saëns's *The Carnival of the Animals*, Desenne joyfully illustrates the song's bestiary, including 'clouds of green chirping parakeets, the solitary whistles of a hawk, the mooing of a little calf; images and dances floating in a dreamy collage reminiscent of similar songs from the stunningly beautiful regions of the Venezuelan plains.'

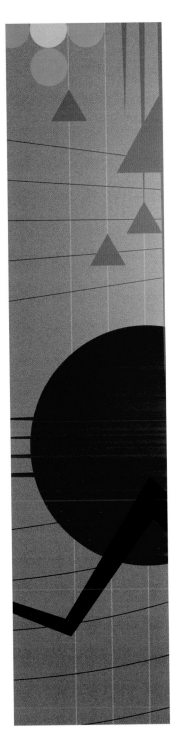

ALBERTO GINASTERA

(1916–83)

Ollantay (1947)
London premiere

PROM 24 • 2 AUGUST

Alberto Ginastera, whose centenary is celebrated this year, was a pioneer of Argentine music and one of Ástor Piazzolla's teachers. At the end of the Second World War, in his late twenties, he took up an invitation from Aaron Copland to study at Tanglewood through a Guggenheim Fellowship, shortly after which he completed the composition of *Ollantay*.

The piece is a continuous three-movement symphonic poem drawing on Quechuan mythology to tell the story of the son of the earth: his defeat by Inca, son of the sun, and his prophecy of the Incan empire's demise.

Ginastera writes in an epic style, somewhere between the glittering and muscular orchestration of Glière's heroic tone-poems and the American 'New Deal' of Copland's *Rodeo*, full of character motifs, jagged ostinatos and sweeping themes.

This was one of Ginastera's last works to integrate Argentine folk music in a relatively straightforward manner – it has a broadly nationalist style. These influences became less obvious and more abstract in his later work, when the music of Bartók and Dallapiccola took on more of a guiding role, and he moved first to the USA and later to Europe following the *coup d'état* of the Argentine Revolution.

HELEN GRIME

(BORN 1981)

Two Eardley Pictures (2016)
BBC commission: world premiere

PROMS 27 & 30 • 5 & 7 AUGUST

Helen Grime's double commission has become a return to her roots, as she formerly played oboe in the National Youth Orchestra of Scotland. 'My childhood was spent in North-East Scotland and Edinburgh,' she recalls. Now based in London, she says she's 'evaluating my Scottishness. I miss the country.'

This commission involves two short pieces, that can be performed either together or separately (as at these two Proms). 'The first ends dramatically and the second can pick up immediately from there. I'm using the same materials for both, but in different ways,' she explains.

Joan Eardley's snow-blanketed landscapes of the far North-East, with their open spaces, etched features of harsh weather and bleak beauty, have been one source of inspiration. Others include the traditions of pibroch (pipers' music) and of 'bothy ballads', songs sung by farm labourers. One of these, 'The Skranky Black Farmer', sits underneath the music, buried in the orchestra's crust. 'It's not so obvious that you'll whistle it afterwards,' says Grime. 'I mined it for harmonic ideas, rhythmic shifts, resonances and other raw materials, so you might say it's in the orchestra's unconscious – although it might yet emerge in one of the sections. Like a sculptor, I work the material to find the essence of my music, including here, its Scottish bedrock.'

GÉRARD GRISEY

(1946–98)

Dérives (1973–4)
UK premiere

PROM 46 • 20 AUGUST

'We are musicians and our model is sound not literature, sound not mathematics, sound not theatre, visual arts, quantum physics, geology, astrology or acupuncture.' Influenced by his teacher Messiaen and Stockhausen among others, Gérard Grisey sought to compose outwards from sound itself, using the technologies of microphones and sound-analysis to hear a new potential in music, one built on the theme of sound as constantly in motion, changing, becoming different, unstable. A pioneer of what became known as Spectral music, he died unexpectedly in 1998, at the age of 52.

Dérives is Grisey's earliest Spectral work, receiving its UK premiere here over 40 years after its composition. He uses a small ensemble alongside the orchestra to add 'space and depth to the sound event', creating effects of almost imperceptible transitions to put into effect the work's dual meanings – of 'drift', as the music veers from the course it appears to chart, and of 'deriving' from a single sound source.

He described the effect as of 'a sea … becoming a tempest, but whose waves would solidify little by little, ultimately heard as the cracking of icebergs overlapping … until arriving in silence.'

HK GRUBER

(BORN 1943)

Busking (2007)
London premiere

PROM 34 • 10 AUGUST

All manner of music and inspiration brew in HK Gruber's work, a cooking pot for unlikely ingredients, where the resulting dishes surprise and always delight. *Busking* is no exception, an off-kilter street concerto for trumpet, banjo, accordion and string orchestra that reels through jazzy riffs, sparkling and sinuous string lines, driving bass and a troupe of dancing motifs. Written for his friend and collaborator, Håkan Hardenberger, playing E flat trumpet, flugelhorn and C trumpet across the work's three movements, *Busking* also toys with music from Gruber's comic opera *Der Herr Nordwind* ('Mr North Wind') and *Three MOB Pieces* (also being performed in PCM 4).

A further point of inspiration is Picasso's *Three Musicians*, showing Harlequin on clarinet, a guitarist Pierrot and a singing monk. They're thought to represent Picasso himself and his poet friends Max Jacob and Guillaume Apollinaire – who had died a few years previously. It's tempting to see in this motley trio a parallel with Gruber's brothers-in-arms, Kurt Schwertsik and Otto Zykan, a riotous assembly of composers grouped with others as the Third Viennese School.

Gruber and his friends, however, reflect a Vienna as melting pot for elements across the former empire, not the centre of a new musical republic. Gruber's music is a goulash for our time and all the tastier for it.

GEORG FRIEDRICH HAAS

(BORN 1953)

Open Spaces II (2007)
UK premiere

PROMS AT … ROUNDHOUSE, CAMDEN • 20 AUGUST

'My music is sound for the sake of perceptual insight – some kind of perceptual revelation.' This credo from the composer James Tenney could just as easily stand for the music of Georg Friedrich Haas, whose *Open Spaces II* is dedicated to the American and adopts a number of Tenney's techniques, exploring the sensual possibilities within sound, alongside Haas's own method developed from close study of composers who have placed a stethoscopic ear to the inner treasures of harmonic colour. Strings and percussion – here distributed around a space in four groups – create a kind of chromatic rhythm through special tuning and overtones, carefully nuanced dynamics and trilling and tremolo effects.

Light and darkness, with all their ethical and political implications, figure prominently in Haas's work. He attributes this to the mountainous Austrian landscape in which he grew up, although he is drawn to an intensity of experience that he also hears in the tradition from Mozart and Schubert to Schreker, and in poetry from Hölderlin to Jon Fosse. This incandescent quality places great responsibilities on the players, but, as Haas notes, 'My music is still utopian, it cannot always be fully realised, but after five or 10 years it becomes possible – by then word has got around and the music has become firmly established.'

TOM HARROLD

(BORN 1991)

Raze (2016)
BBC commission: world premiere

PROM 75 • 10 SEPTEMBER

Following the success of the Proms Youth Ensemble's performance at last year's festival alongside the Aurora Orchestra, which included Anna Meredith's *Smatter Hauler*, fellow Scot Tom Harrold has been invited to write a showcase piece featuring the group.

Since winning the BBC Proms/ *Guardian* Young Composer Competition and completing his studies at the Royal Northern College of Music, Harrold has been in demand, writing a flurry of orchestral works and *Darkened Dreams* for the Proms in 2014, using recordings of favourite sounds submitted by listeners to Radio 4's *PM*.

Raze is unusual for Harrold in being propelled by its title. 'Titles almost always come at the end of composing for me,' he says. Its meanings of 'clear the way', 'overthrow' and 'knock down' 'convey exactly what I wanted for a noisy, carnival-like concert such as the Last Night of the Proms,' he enthuses. 'The piece uses sour, baleful strings, blaring brass and cacophonous, raucous winds, which "raise", soar and hurtle towards the climax.'

Harrold wants the young players of the Ensemble to contribute to the party atmosphere of the Last Night. 'I really see the piece as a celebration of the Proms Youth Ensemble, so my focus is on writing a piece they will enjoy performing.'

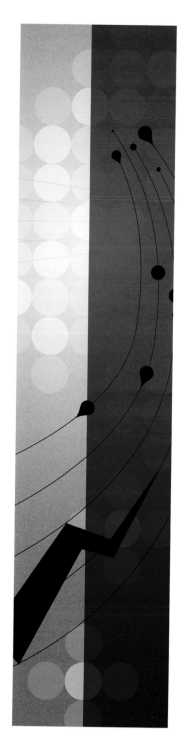

MALCOLM HAYES

(BORN 1951)

Violin Concerto (2015)
BBC commission: world premiere

PROM 35 • 11 AUGUST

Writing his first concerto, receiving its premiere from the stunning violinist Tai Murray, Malcolm Hayes was seeking an 'open-air quality', reflecting in part on the years he spent living and working in the Outer Hebrides around the late 1970s. It was a time of recuperation and also of convivial living, not simply a retreat into the Scottish wilds, even as it presaged a later pause in composing to concentrate on writing and music criticism.

This perspective from the UK's geographical margins nevertheless speaks of the dialogue Hayes's music has with tradition. Not seeking the spotlight, he is interested in what he calls a 'long-perspective music', drawing on the legacy of Sibelius for this concerto, as much as on the dramatic form established by Mozart and Beethoven. Written as a set of double variations and covering a single 25-minute span, it weaves a course through the tripartite journey broadly corresponding to exposition, development and reprise, the solo violin 'soaring in the outer sections and engaging the orchestra in the middle'.

This image of the 'soaring' violin line might recall Vaughan Williams's *The Lark Ascending*, but Hayes qualifies this. 'The soloist doesn't represent a bird. But it does convey, perhaps, a life-form in flight' – a chance, then, for Murray to take wing.

PIERS HELLAWELL

(BORN 1956)

Wild Flow (2016)
BBC commission: world premiere

PROM 47 • 21 AUGUST

At first listen, Piers Hellawell's multi-movement works can be a puzzle. He eschews a binding logic, the familiar musical narratives that guide us to the safe harbour of a secure conclusion. 'These works, especially those in my *Sound Carvings* series, have long preferred a zigzag progression to the cumulative progression of post-Romantic music.'

What 'flows' here is the orchestra, as Hellawell works with the grain rather than forcing it to take alien shape. 'The orchestra is my instrument, but my treatment has definitely changed,' he says. Where a decade ago he could write each instrument as a solo contributor, now 'individual parts are subsumed into a shared expression: my orchestra is becoming a less separable entity.'

Wild Flow's sequence of five sections presents a sustained slow central movement surrounded by more energetic segments, obliquely linked to the moods of church canticles Hellawell remembers from his youth.

'As I worked on *Wild Flow*, I was also aware of heading towards 60 and mentally discarding some unwanted baggage from a mixed decade; it's hugely upbeat stuff.' The scattered seeds of childhood's wild flowers have taken root.

EMILY HOWARD

(BORN 1979)

Torus (2016)
BBC commission: world premiere

PROM 53 • 25 AUGUST

'The support I've received from the Royal Liverpool Philharmonic Orchestra and Vasily Petrenko has been fantastic – it means so much to me that they'll premiere *Torus* at the BBC Proms. I grew up around Liverpool and the RLPO's sound and look defined the symphony orchestra for me in my formative years.'

Torus is Emily Howard's seventh orchestral work with a scientific title, but this fascination with pattern and structure – by a former junior chess champion – shouldn't mislead. For, just as scientists have been fascinated by the poetry of life in search of universal truths, she – like so many composers before her – listens for the poetry in science, its concepts and language, to create unique experiences. 'I'm fascinated by morphology, how forces interacting create shape,' she says. 'I like to write very direct music with stark contrasts.'

A whole with a hole, the torus is often described as doughnut-shaped, a squashed and stretched ball held together by a central void. 'I believe my music is often more about absence than presence,' says Howard, adding dramatically: 'and here I'm almost imagining the torus as a sphere with its heart ripped out. I'm drawn to the idea of a toric music – torus-shaped journeys in sound.'

THOMAS LARCHER

(BORN 1963)

Symphony No. 2 (2016)
UK premiere

PROM 57 • 28 AUGUST

One of Europe's leading mid-generation composers, Thomas Larcher writes works that emerge from the tensions between re-evaluating tradition and avoiding obvious conventions and formulas. He notes that 'tonal principles never really disappeared', but now that they can be used unselfconsciously, what does it mean to deploy them today? 'It cannot be the same after Gil Evans, after Spectral music or after Terry Riley's *In C*,' he argues. The forms built from tonality also need to be reinvented, just as historic houses have been wired for electric lighting.

His instrumentation is 'classical', albeit supplemented by the flotsam and jetsam of more recent acquisitions, such as oil barrels, automobile springs and biscuit boxes. 'This piece is very much about different forms of energy,' Larcher says. 'Either bundled or scattered, smooth, energetic or furious. Especially furious!'

Originally conceived as a Concerto for Orchestra, Larcher's Symphony No. 2 has the expected four movements, although the mobility of his concerto idea also simmers underneath, skittering between chamber music to full orchestra, pulling in different directions or moving as one. On finding an idiom that speaks today, he co-opts Samuel Beckett, adding: 'As always, it's about trying, failing trying again and failing better.'

REINBERT DE LEEUW

(BORN 1938)

Der nächtliche Wanderer (2013)
UK premiere

PROM 26 • 4 AUGUST

Having ceased composing some 40 years ago to focus on conducting and performing, Reinbert de Leeuw found his late return to composition both surprising and liberating. 'I was constantly in doubt,' he says and yet 'musical, obsessive things' insisted on intruding into this work.

Der nächtliche Wanderer is haunted by one of Wagner's last compositions, his *Elegy* for piano, Galina Ustvolskaya's Violin Sonata, and a short work of the German poet-philosopher Friedrich Hölderlin, which also gave de Leeuw his spectral title. These layers grip the orchestra's circling melodies, the darker currents of its harmonies and the rhythmic flow of its statements. Yet it's the sound-world that is immediately striking and vivid. Alongside the orchestra, all three elements are played as recordings (albeit transcribed for other instruments), as is the opening barking of a dog, placing us in some twilit zone. Meanwhile, an off-stage group adds to the sense of mysterious, brooding absence.

Charles Ives's influence also looms large. His *Three Places in New England* 'was the shock that set me free, showing me how to contrast the complex and the simple. It changed my life.' The drama of this 'Night Wanderer' is that a musical revelation in the 1970s has resurfaced, transfigured by half a lifetime's immersion in others' music.

MAGNUS LINDBERG

(BORN 1958)

New work (2016)
BBC co-commission with the London Philharmonic Orchestra, Helsinki Festival & Casa da Música, Porto: world premiere

PROM 13 • 24 JULY

It's over 30 years since *Kraft*, a slab of raw musical energy, thrust Magnus Lindberg forwards as a major orchestral composer, a reputation he has consolidated ever since. This new work comes from his residency with the London Philharmonic Orchestra. 'It gives me an insight into the musicians, people who become friends,' he says. 'It's like writing for a person.'

The pairing of the premiere with Beethoven's Ninth Symphony also plays its part. Lindberg explains: 'I've spent a lot of time with the score, making charts of the rhythmic structure, getting inside that world. It's wild!' That unleashed freedom resonates with his early work, its rhythmic and percussive energy, on which he's also been reflecting. Finding a fresh directness for last year's Carnegie Hall opener, *Vivo*, Lindberg is searching for a similar synthesis with the sophisticated harmonic language of his later music. 'The performance in the Royal Albert Hall is very special; I imagine filling that great space with sound.'

At the time of *Kraft*, Lindberg claimed 'only the extreme is interesting', although now he says, 'I'm more realistic. But expression as such should be extreme. Fantasies, illusions, things unheard – these are all important. I'm interested in the big contrasts, creating tension and dramaturgy.' It promises to start this Prom off with a bang.

COLIN MATTHEWS

(BORN 1946)

Berceuse for Dresden (2005)
London premiere

PROM 41 • 16 AUGUST

Commissioned for the reconsecration of the rebuilt Frauenkirche in 2005, the ruins of which had been left as a memorial until German reunification, Colin Matthews's *Berceuse for Dresden* is dedicated to the memory of Victor Klemperer. The Jewish diarist, veteran of the Great War and cousin of the conductor Otto Klemperer, used the chaos of the Allied bombardment to escape with his wife, avoiding imminent deportation to the camps.

Matthews based the music 'almost entirely on the sounds of the eight bells of the Frauenkirche, their pitches transformed into long melodic lines for the solo cello, while the overtones of the bells provide the underlying harmony.' This 'berceuse' – a cradlesong – marking the cathedral's rebirth is not innocent, but hard-won, a focus of civic worship born with a long memory. The mood is impassioned as well as lyrical, with the cello featuring in particular in 'the role almost of a wordless singer'.

'I've never written a piece that was so site- and occasion-specific before or since, so finding the appropriate mood wasn't easy,' Matthews recalls. 'The first performance was an extraordinary occasion, very emotional and a huge thing to be part of.' As the *Berceuse* builds to a stunning climax sustaining a halo of the bells' harmonics, we can feel that for ourselves.

MARLOS NOBRE

(BORN 1939)

Kabbalah (2004)
UK premiere

PROM 51 • 24 AUGUST

Considered by many as the successor to Villa-Lobos, Marlos Nobre is one of Brazil's most distinguished composers, as well as being a well-regarded conductor and pianist – not least by his friends and mentors, Yehudi Menuhin and Arthur Rubinstein.

Alongside his search for new harmonic possibilities inspired by Debussy, Bartók and Lutosławski, Nobre acknowledges the influence of the Afro-Brazilian rhythms of Recife, his home town in the country's North-East, including the maracatu, the frevo, the caboclinhos, the candomblé and the cirandas.

Nobre wrote *Kabbalah* following extensive study of Jewish sources, translating its principles into his own musical ideas. 'According to the kabbalistic science, everything we want is light and energy,' he explains. 'But for me, as a composer, the most important concept is that imagination and inspiration represent the basic truths and unlock the unseen wonders of the universe.'

The piece similarly contrasts two types of material: 'light', which is lyrical, chromatic and draws on contrasts of instrumental colour; and 'energy', giving full play to Nobre's rhythmic invention and flair for musical drama, at times sounding like a Brazilian incarnation of Stravinsky's *The Rite of Spring*.

BAYAN NORTHCOTT

(BORN 1940)

Concerto for Orchestra (2015)
BBC commission: world premiere

PROM 62 • 31 AUGUST

'There are no extra-musical ideas behind my piece. It's music about music – about my own thematic ideas and the music of the composers I love,' explains Bayan Northcott. 'I don't mind if listeners detect traces of Machaut or Purcell, Haydn or Brahms, Mahler or Sibelius, Stravinsky, Tippett or Britten. My hope is to have drawn something fresh and personal from such influences.'

Active for almost 40 years as a music critic of the *New Statesman*, *Sunday Telegraph* and *The Independent*, Northcott was a late starter and mostly self-taught as a composer. Although he has written substantial pieces such as his Concerto for Horn and Ensemble (1998), the new Concerto for Orchestra is his belated first completed score for full orchestra.

Written as a compact three-movement form played without a break, the concerto follows a traditional model of a sonata-form opening that develops two contrasting themes, an Adagio of alternating variations, and a 'frisky rondo finale'.

Taking a long view, Northcott claims that his goal is 'to wrest something new from the inherited procedures of Western tradition'.

ANTHONY PAYNE

(BORN 1936)

Of Land, Sea and Sky (2016)
BBC commission: world premiere

PROM 15 • 26 JULY

'I owe the BBC a great deal – they've commissioned all of my significant pieces. I'm 80 this year and I see this as the climax of my works with the BBC.' *Of Land, Sea and Sky* is, then, a landmark work for Anthony Payne, marking a close relationship with the BBC orchestras spanning more than 30 years, from *The Spirit's Harvest* and *Time's Arrow*, through to *Visions and Journeys* and *Period of Cosmography*. There's much more to Payne than his completion of Elgar's Third Symphony.

Payne has long been fascinated by nature's trickery, examples here guiding the work's eight sections that flow unbroken with texts of his own devising. His mental pocket-book of ideas include a fleeting televisual image of horses galloping as if on water, though only at ocean's edge; a ship's captain imagined by Joseph Conrad espying crags through a storm, shuddering to find instead a tsunami; clouds above a gentle landscape becoming, on closer inspection, the smoke of gunfire in a Somme painting by the Australian Impressionist, Arthur Streeton; and the illusory perspective from a train window, as foreground races past whilst distant hills appear unmoving.

Nature's illusions, then, or human folly? As in Vaughan Williams's music, the pastoral includes shadowed valleys as well as sunlit peaks.

DAVID SAWER

(BORN 1961)

April \ March (2014)
BBC co-commission with the Royal Philharmonic Society: world premiere

PROMS AT ... ROUNDHOUSE, CAMDEN • 20 AUGUST

'I've wanted to write for dance, especially classically-trained dancers, for some time,' says David Sawer. 'They bring a different energy, a concern for shape, a grace and rhythm.' Commissioned through the Foundation of the late Proms Director John Drummond, which stipulated a dance element, he knew immediately that he wanted to work with the Royal Ballet and choreographer Aletta Collins.

He has in mind an 'abstract ballet', without narrative but with a clearly defined structure. *April \ March* will exist first as a concert piece, premiered at the Proms by the London Sinfonietta. 'I'm thinking of the musicians as a small orchestra rather than an ensemble,' he explains. 'The music needs to work both in its own right and for a stage pit. It will have kinetic rhythm.'

Given Sawer's predisposition towards the stage – he's previously described himself as 'a theatre person' – it's perhaps surprising that this will be only his second work conceived for dance (after *Rumpelstiltskin* in 2009). When composing, he always has in mind the physicality of the space, of the performers, the relationships, and of the listening experience. His music has an exquisite sense of timing and a musical theatricality, as well as a purity of sound. Sir John would surely have approved.

IRIS TER SCHIPHORST

(BORN 1956)

Gravitational Waves (2016)
BBC co-commission with the National Youth Orchestra of Great Britain: London premiere

PROM 29 • 6 AUGUST

The National Youth Orchestra of Great Britain's commissioned works showcase a new generation of composers keen to push the boundaries, and often pursuing apparently divergent musical interests. Iris ter Schiphorst's piece follows on from those by Anna Meredith, Larry Goves and Tansy Davies – like them, ter Schiphorst has combined composition (and work as a classical pianist) with playing in bands as a bass player, drummer, on keyboards and as sound engineer.

Her piece was also commissioned to complement Holst's *The Planets*, which by coincidence she was planning to explore with her students in Vienna. 'Through my teaching of "applied music", I am very close to the musical experience of young people who do not listen to classical music every day,' she says, adding that Holst's film-like music is 'a fantastic way to reach young audiences'. At the same time, ter Schiphorst's music, with her use of sampling, spiked rhythms and vivid orchestration, belongs completely to our time, 55 years since the first manned spaceflight.

'The musicians at the NYO are so talented,' she enthuses. 'But I hope to include some nice surprises for them which are not "standard". Maybe there are some challenges they are not yet so familiar with, but I am sure we will have a very good time together exploring the piece.'

MARK SIMPSON

(BORN 1988)

Israfel (2014)
London premiere

PROM 33 • 9 AUGUST

At 27, Mark Simpson has already been composing for more than half his life, but that doesn't mean it gets easier. 'Unless I feel it physically inside, that raw, visceral response to something, I can't get into the music.'

Following a struggle with his previous piece and feeling constrained by the system he was using, Simpson approached *Israfel* needing to let his music run freely. Edgar Allan Poe's poem of the Koranic angel resonated with him and that sense of liberation bursts through the music, especially in the second half of the piece as it takes flight, airborne.

Poe's *Israfel* is stirred by music, the lyre 'by which he sits and sings – / The trembling living wire / Of those unusual strings.' 'Composers now usually divide the strings. I wanted a big, long melody, unison in the strings,' says Simpson. 'It sings all the time.'

This *Israfel* is not specifically a religious expression, nor a representation of the angel's trumpeting. 'It was the emotional response to the idea of an all-encompassing higher being of music that was important to me, a figure of apocalypse perhaps, but also one of hope.' *Israfel* gives us just such a trembling ecstasy, a rapturous strain of melodising.

HUW WATKINS

(BORN 1976)

Cello Concerto (2016)
BBC commission: world premiere

PROM 37 • 12 AUGUST

Composer-pianist Huw Watkins and cellist-conductor Paul Watkins are brothers from a musical family and they've been playing together from childhood.

'I'm biased of course, but there's no cellist I know who makes a more expressive, beautiful sound than Paul and I have that very much in mind while writing the piece,' says Huw. 'I've written more for him than for anyone else – solo pieces, cello-and-piano music and even a mini-concerto for him with the Nash Ensemble. But this is the first time I've had the chance to write a full-scale concerto with Paul at the heart of it.'

It's the brothers' long experience of performing chamber music together that gives this new work an uncommon intimacy and that marks it out from Huw's previous concertos – a form of which he's particularly fond.

'I have a feeling that, despite the sheer size of the Royal Albert Hall, very quiet music will have a remarkable ability to draw you in.' This transference of imaginative space is something music can accomplish to uncanny effect – so that, while listening in a hall with 5,000 others and hundreds of thousands on the radio, we can nevertheless be party to a musical journey begun in a sitting room in South Wales.

JÖRG WIDMANN

(BORN 1973)

Armonica (2006)
UK premiere

PROM 23 • 1 AUGUST

Jörg Widmann is renowned for bringing new life to the legacy of works by Mozart, Beethoven, Schubert and Schumann among others, both as a celebrated clarinettist and as a composer of intensely direct music. Commissioned to write for Salzburg's Mozart Festival, he turned to his illustrious forebear's last chamber work, a quintet featuring glass harmonica, fascinated by the instrument's resonant possibilities.

It was Benjamin Franklin's mechanised system of 1761 – using rotating pitched glass rubbed with moistened fingers – that popularised the ethereal sound of the glass harmonica, bringing it to the attention of composers such as Mozart and Beethoven. It subsequently fell out of favour as its delicate sound struggled in the larger halls that opened to accommodate the growing public for concert music, the vibration of its solid objects melting all too easily into air.

Widmann doesn't imitate Mozart in *Armonica*, but rather explores the instrument's timbre, blending it with accordion and water gongs in a colouristic orchestration. 'The basic idea is to translate this gentle swelling out of nothingness, which characterises the glass harmonica's sound, into orchestral terms,' he has explained. 'The aim is to create a sound-world that is as light as possible, that seems to be weightless.'

TWO-PART HARMONY

As John Wilson and his orchestra celebrate the 120th anniversary of Ira Gershwin's birth, **David Benedict** pays tribute to the two brothers who formed one of America's most celebrated and dynamic song-writing duos

Popular music isn't short of singing siblings – think The Partridge Family, The Osmonds, The Jacksons and the von Trapps – but it's rare to find musical writing talent whose creations outlive their original recordings. The great exception? Step forwards George and Ira Gershwin. It's their songs that form the backbone of this year's Prom with John Wilson and his all-star orchestra.

Scholarly and calm, Ira (originally Israel) was born on New York's Lower East Side in 1896. His brother Jacob, forever known as George, arrived two years later. Temperamentally, George could not have been more different, growing up with scattershot energy, racing around, unable to settle. Until, that is, he discovered music via a violin-prodigy schoolfriend. By 15, he had absorbed enough from piano teachers to quit school for a job as a song-plugger, playing at a Tin Pan Alley music-publishing house, promoting songs. His weekly wage was $15. Ira was earning the same: as a cashier at the Lafayette Baths, one of two New York bathhouses run by their father Morris.

George almost immediately began song-writing, with Ira supplying lyrics. Their first proper song, 'The Real American Folk Song (Is a Rag)', made it to Broadway on 24 October 1918 … but the star singer soon ditched it. Exactly a year later, George's song 'Swanee', with a lyric by Irving Caesar, appeared in the show *Demi-Tasse*. Al Jolson took a fancy to it and recorded it in 1920, giving 21-year-old George $10,000 royalties for its first year's sales alone.

By 1928, George and Ira had an astonishing three shows running concurrently on Broadway, featuring such enduring marvels as 'Lady, Be Good, 'Funny Face', ''S Wonderful' and 'Someone to

Watch Over Me'. Not everything, however, was an instant smash. 'The Man I Love' was cut from three successive musicals. George later observed, 'It lacks a soothing, seducing rhythm and it has a certain slow lilt that subtly disturbs the audience instead of lulling it into acceptance. Then, too, there is the melody which is not easy to catch; it presents too many chromatic pitfalls. Hardly anybody whistles or hums it correctly without the support of a piano or other instrument.'

Nevertheless, this idiosyncratic number became one of George and Ira's signature pieces, thanks to the musical build-up of intense yearning in the accompaniment's descending harmony. Such emotional depth dictates the mood of its lyrics: indeed, all their songs began with the music. Ira summed up his job as 'fitting words mosaically to music already composed'. True though that is, George's respect for Ira meant that he constantly sought his elder brother's approval for what he was writing and would not stop reworking until Ira was happy.

Unlike Ira, who focused solely on song-writing, George had several separate careers, taking jazz into the concert hall with *Rhapsody in Blue*; becoming an exuberant orchestral writer (as in *An American in Paris*); and as the composer whose first and only full-length opera, *Porgy and Bess*, is one of the undisputed masterpieces of 20th-century music-theatre.

Ten months after the premiere of *Porgy and Bess* in October 1935, George and Ira flew to Los Angeles. Back in 1931, the Fox movie studio had binned almost the entire score for their first picture, *Delicious*, but now, as they took up residence at 1019 North Roxbury Drive in Beverly Hills – where the composer

Arnold Schoenberg turned up once a week to play tennis with George – matters improved exponentially. In rapid succession they wrote scores for the Fred Astaire/Ginger Rogers film *Shall We Dance* (for which George also did the orchestral scoring, a job usually handled by studio music staff), *A Damsel in Distress* and *The Goldwyn Follies*.

The fearsome intensity at which George wrote was giving him crippling headaches – at least that was what his friends and doctors said following years of George complaining. He entered Cedars of Lebanon Hospital on 26 June 1937 and left after three days of tests. On Friday 9 July he fell unconscious and was re-admitted. A five-hour brain operation in the early hours of Sunday morning revealed an inoperable brain tumour. At 10.35am he died.

Ira was devastated. For several years he resisted all calls to return to professional writing. When he did return, in 1941, it was with the best available talent. He teamed up with Kurt Weill for the musical (and subsequent movie) *Lady in the Dark* and for the musical based on Benvenuto Cellini's vainglorious memoirs, *The Firebrand of Florence*; and with Jerome Kern for the Rita Hayworth/Gene Kelly movie *Cover Girl* and, most famously, the peerless Judy Garland/James Mason film *A Star Is Born*.

But that's not the whole story. Hollywood maintained its love for the Gershwins and made the (madly fictionalised) 1945 biopic *Rhapsody in Blue*, while Ira himself had a posthumous collaboration adding lyrics to 11 of George's unused melodies for the 1947 Betty Grable picture *The Shocking Miss Pilgrim*.

Most of the opulent Hollywood arrangements which John Wilson and his orchestra perform

Gene Kelly in the 1951 movie *An American in Paris*, which featured nine of George and Ira's songs, as well as Kelly's choreography of George's popular symphonic poem that gave the movie its name

in their Prom have not been played live since the original recording sessions, not least because most of the scores were destroyed. It's thanks to some painstaking reconstruction work, under Wilson's supervision, that Proms audiences will hear these in concert for the first time. 'Restoring lost scores is part of a longstanding project in my spare time,' says Wilson. 'It's an ongoing necessity.' ●

David Benedict is a broadcaster and critic specialising in musical theatre. He is currently writing the authorised biography of Stephen Sondheim for Random House/Pan Macmillan.

George and Ira Gershwin Rediscovered
Featuring original orchestrations from the Hollywood film musicals

PROM 38 • 13 AUGUST

LATIN LEADERS

In the summer in which Brazil hosts the Olympic Games, **Neil Fisher** looks behind the surge in the classical music scene in Latin America as a number of South American orchestras, soloists and composers appear at the Proms

This summer British athletes are heading for Rio de Janeiro – but South America is also sending some of its finest performers to the Royal Albert Hall. From Venezuela comes the Simón Bolívar Symphony Orchestra under Gustavo Dudamel and from Brazil the São Paulo Symphony Orchestra, led by Marin Alsop with the Venezuelan pianist Gabriela Montero in tow. Along with works by Grieg, Rachmaninov and Ravel, both orchestras are bringing new music from their own countries and both celebrate Brazil's national composer, Heitor Villa-Lobos. It's confirmation, if it were needed, that if classical music were an Olympic sport, South America would definitely be moving up the medal table.

On the surface, there is not much in common between the two orchestras. For the Paulistas (as those from Brazil's largest city of São Paulo are known) this is a second date, after the São Paulo Symphony Orchestra performed at the Proms in 2012, when the Olympic Games were held in London. It did not celebrate its Proms debut – as the Simón Bolívar orchestra did in 2007 – with the players revealing their national colours on reversible jackets or twirling their double basses. But, if the orchestra from São Paulo makes a more sober impression, that's partly deliberate. 'A lot of people expect us to be a Latin American, colourful, light-music kind of orchestra, and then they get a surprise,' says the orchestra's artistic director, Arthur Nestrovski.

Visiting the orchestra's home, a former coffee exchange, you admire the sense of seclusion: a rare commodity in a city of 20 million people, choked by such bad traffic that the wealthy prefer to travel by helicopter. Yet there is much more to classical music in São Paulo – and Brazil – than what goes on there. The São Paulo SO regularly decamps to other parts of the city and, as part of a series of concerts to welcome Marin Alsop, it performed Shostakovich's Fifth Symphony (shorn of its anguished slow movement) in a city park to 15,000 people. I watched it in the company of frisbee-throwers, dog-walkers and barely dressed sun-worshippers. Shostakovich might have been baffled; however, the truncated symphony still caused tingles in the midst of this *al fresco* party.

Nor is the São Paulo SO ignoring a wider mission – the same one that underpins the Simón Bolívar Symphony Orchestra, which began as an amateur group nurtured through Venezuela's education scheme, El Sistema. 'Brazilians think of themselves as Brazilian, not Latin American,' says Nestrovski. 'But we have to change. We have to start thinking about ourselves as an orchestra with a role to play in this continent.' As well as subsidising its

" The touchpaper has been lit and the Sistema message is spreading. "

flagship orchestra, the state of São Paulo supports some 400 different music schools. The São Paulo SO is a parent organisation to one of the city's rising youth orchestras, the Sinfônica Heliópolis, whose players come from a notorious *favela* (slum). Elsewhere in Brazil, the state of Bahia (around the size of Spain) has its own musical education scheme directly modelled on the Venezuelan one. Called Neojiba, it supports three youth orchestras, a choir and a classical music radio station. The touchpaper has been lit and the Sistema message is spreading.

Sir Simon Rattle has suggested that the success of the Sistema is partly down to the fact that teenagers in South America have fewer distractions than Europeans and can focus on music more easily. Yet there are still plenty of reasons in Venezuela and Brazil why your average teen might overlook classical music. First, there's the cult of football. And there are plenty of other genres of Latin and Brazilian music that are practised with the same zeal and sophistication as Western classical.

The Sistema has one answer: grab the foot soldiers early. In Venezuela, at any performance by one of the flagship orchestras, there will always be a group of Sistema novices, usually children under the age of 8, who are awestruck to see their heroes at such close quarters (cue raucous, partisan cheering). This exposure to the elite ensures that new audiences are built as well as orchestras. But it's also about competition and the drive to do better.

A former player in the Simón Bolívar SO, Christian Vásquez left the orchestra to conduct another Sistema band, the Teresa Carreño Youth Orchestra of Venezuela and now tours the world with it. When I asked him how he rated his teenage players, he said: 'When we were the same age in the Simón Bolívar as the players of the Teresa Carreño are now, we just didn't play as well. In Venezuela, we're seeing the evolution of musicians.' The hunger to be the best – cheered on from the sidelines by your friends and peers – is what drives these performers. And, as any Olympic athlete knows, why settle for silver when you could have gold? ●

Neil Fisher has written for *The Times* since 2004 and has reported on classical music around the world, including visits to Caracas in Venezuela and São Paulo and Salvador in Brazil. He has also contributed to *Gramophone, Esquire* and BBC Radio 4.

Brazilian athlete Alan Fonteles Cardoso Oliveira, who won gold in the T44 200m race at the London 2012 Paralympic Games

Works for 12 cellos, including music by Villa-Lobos
PROMS CHAMBER MUSIC 2 • 25 JULY

Ginastera Ollantay *London premiere*
PROM 24 • 2 AUGUST

Gabriela Montero *piano*, São Paulo Symphony Orchestra/Marin Alsop Including music by Villa-Lobos and Marlos Nobre
PROM 51 • 24 AUGUST

São Paulo Symphony Orchestra, São Paulo Jazz Symphony Orchestra/Marin Alsop Including Brazilian popular music
PROM 52 • 24 AUGUST

Simón Bolívar Symphony Orchestra/ Gustavo Dudamel Including music by Villa-Lobos and Paul Desenne
PROM 67 • 4 SEPTEMBER

Gareth Copley/Getty Images

PARRY'S 'JERUSALEM'

Marking 100 years since its composition, **Hannah French** charts the history of one of the 'holy trinity' of Last Night staples, revealing its associations with women's suffrage and highlighting its status as an alternative English national anthem

On 10 March 1916 Hubert Parry completed his setting of the opening verses of William Blake's epic poem *Milton*. Entitled 'And did those feet in ancient time', the work was commissioned by Poet Laureate Robert Bridges on behalf of Lieutenant Colonel Sir Francis Younghusband's patriotic campaigning organisation, Fight for Right. Parry's brief was to compose a unison song that an audience would feel compelled to join in and sing, and which would ultimately become an anthem to counteract First World War German propaganda and celebrate Allied victories. Premiered on 28 March 1916, at a Queen's Hall meeting of Fight for Right, by a massed choir of 300 volunteers from London-based choral societies under Henry Walford Davies, it was an instant success. By November Parry had orchestrated the organ accompaniment and retitled the work *Jerusalem* for publication. However, he had always been uneasy with the strong patriotism of Fight for Right and in 1917, after turning down further commissions from the movement to compose more nationalist songs, he wrote to Younghusband to withdraw his support and association.

The nation, however, had already taken to its heart the stirring melody of *Jerusalem*, so Parry was particularly gratified when Millicent Garrett Fawcett of the National Union of Women's Suffrage Societies sought to perform it at a demonstration concert in the Royal Albert Hall on 13 March 1918:

I wish indeed it might become the Women Voters' hymn, as you suggest. People seem to enjoy singing it. And having the vote ought to diffuse a good deal of joy too. So they would combine happily.

Parry had originally intended the first verse to be sung by a solo female voice, so this was a happy union. He granted copyright to the suffragist cause and the popularity of *Jerusalem* increased as it became the anthem of the Women's Institute.

Edward Elgar's enlarged orchestration, made for the 1922 Leeds Festival, only increased *Jerusalem*'s appeal and has become synonymous with the Last Night of the Proms. There have been only two occasions when *Jerusalem* has appeared earlier in the season. The first was its Proms premiere under the baton of Henry Wood, when it was partnered with Parry's *Blest Pair of Sirens* to conclude a 1942 Prom of Wood's own arrangements of Handel and Rameau. The other was in 2009, in a performance by the Ukulele Orchestra of Great Britain, proving the robust nature of its identity. The arrival of Malcolm Sargent in 1947 marked a change in tone for the Last Night and its broadcast on BBC Television. He oversaw the introduction of *Jerusalem* to the programme in 1953, symptomatic of a post-war era of increasingly rambunctious season finales. It has remained a staple of the evening and an expression of Englishness ever since, forming with Elgar's *Pomp and Circumstance* March No. 1 and Henry Wood's *Fantasia on British Sea-Songs* one third of a holy trinity of triumphalist Last Night music.

What Parry captured in his anthem of comfort for war-torn England was a vision of spiritual fervour. One obituary summarised Parry's achievements, plainly evident in *Jerusalem*: 'He represented in music the essential sanity of the English genius: its mixture of strength and tenderness, its breadth, its humour, its entire freedom from vacuity and affectation.' The meaning of Blake's text has, of course,

Women's rights protesters in London, c1910: Parry was happy to grant a request from the National Union of Women's Suffrage Societies that *Jerusalem* 'might become the Women Voters' hymn'

come under regular scrutiny, some examining the apocryphal image of heaven in England, others the potential sexual or chauvinistic connotations of 'arrows of desire', and most forming an opinion on the identity of the 'dark satanic mills'; but the musical setting has rarely been criticised. While the words are open to interpretation, Parry's music has clearly rendered the sentiments decent, God-fearing and magnificent. When introducing *Jerusalem* to his former pupil Henry Walford Davies in 1916, Parry himself pointed to one of the highlights: 'He put his finger on the note D in the second stanza where the words "O clouds unfold" break his rhythm. I do not think any word passed about it, yet he made it perfectly clear that this was the one note and one moment of the song which he treasured.' The collective emotion that sweeps through the raised unison voices of a full hall is an honest elevation of collective hope. Little surprise, then, that *Jerusalem* was the only one of the Last Night trio performed immediately following the tragic events of 11 September

2001, and fitting that, in its centenary year, it has been proposed as a possible national anthem for England. Ultimately *Jerusalem* is the melody that re-echoes at the end of the Last Night – a sentiment foreseen by Henry Wood:

And as each Last Night of the Season has come round and I have been almost mobbed and my car pushed out into Langham Place by a crowd of jolly young men and girls, I have realised increasingly with the years that music is a great power in England: that there are hundreds of young people who have discovered what their fathers discovered – *that the best melodies are in the best music.* ●

Hannah French is a musicologist, lecturer, and broadcaster. She studied Henry Wood's interpretations of J. S. Bach's orchestral works for her PhD and continues to research his archive of scores at the Royal Academy of Music, and his role in the English Bach awakening.

Parry, orch. Elgar Jerusalem
PROM 75 • 10 SEPTEMBER

akg-images

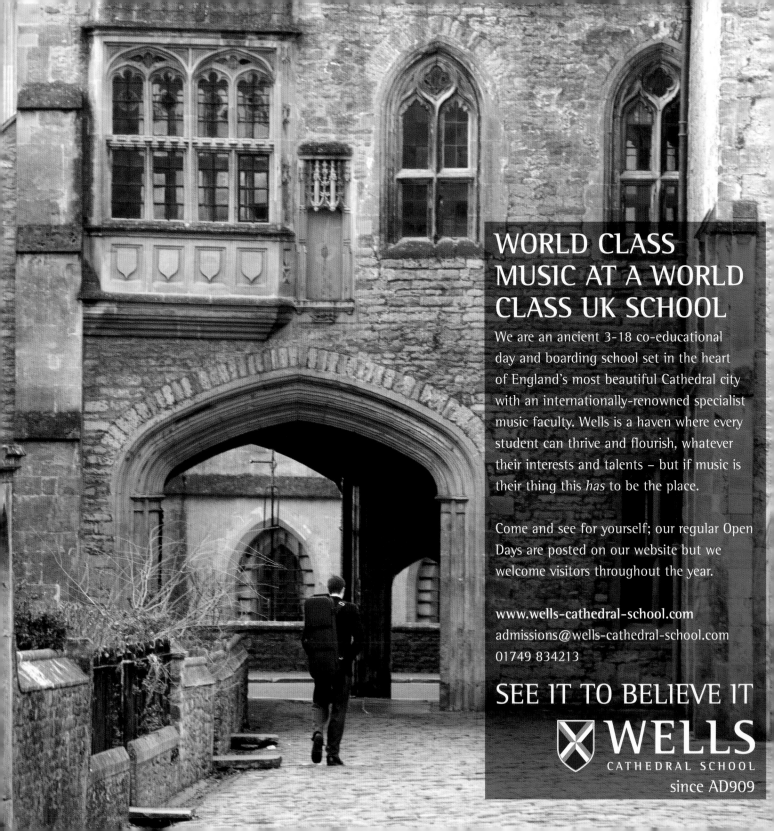

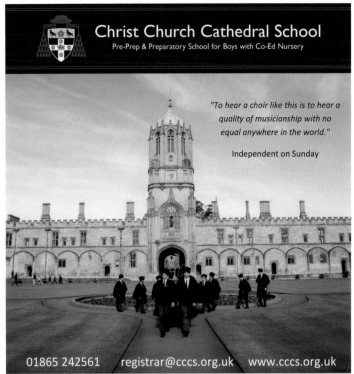
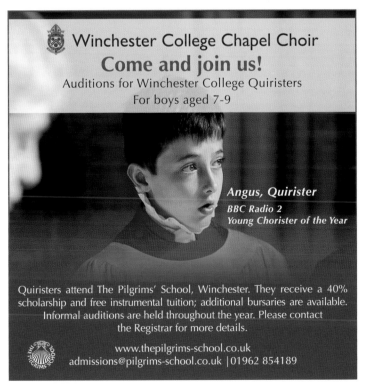
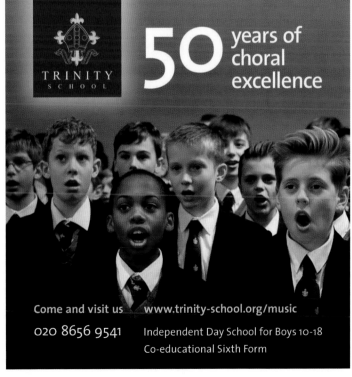

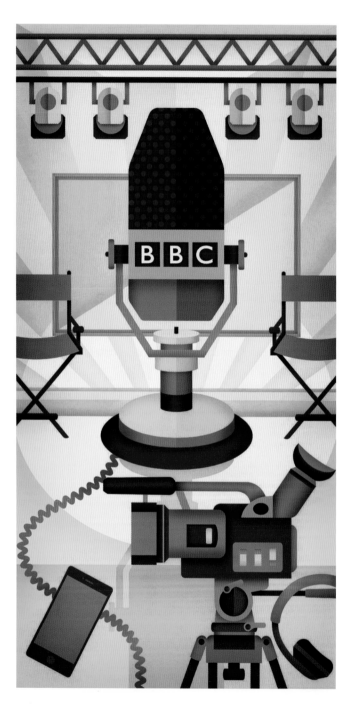

ON TV,
ON RADIO,
ONLINE

Whether it's in the comfort of your home or out on the go, you can watch or listen to the Proms wherever you are – including on your tablet or mobile phone. Plan your summer viewing and listening with this guide to the Proms on the BBC

Since the first radio broadcast of a Promenade concert in 1932, the ways in which you can experience the Proms has grown and evolved to embrace a myriad of platforms on TV, on radio and online, while continuing Henry Wood's vision of bringing the best music to the widest possible audience. Every Prom is broadcast live on Radio 3 and in HD Sound online, with a dedicated team of producers and engineers to ensure that those tuning in have 'the best seat in the house'. It's even easier to access the Proms wherever and whenever you want, with 30-day catch-up available through the Proms website, as well as the Proms on your mobile, where you can create your own Proms playlist, access curated Radio 3 programmes and features and download programmes and concerts on the BBC iPlayer and iPlayer Radio apps.

Feel part of the festival atmosphere in your own home with TV broadcasts on BBC Two, BBC Four and online throughout the summer – including a gala Gershwin evening with the ever-popular John Wilson and his orchestra and BBC Two's weekly magazine show *Proms Extra* with Katie Derham – or you can enjoy the wide range of Proms Extra events, mostly broadcast during the main-evening interval on Radio 3, featuring talks and interviews with artists from across the season, readings from authors and insights into the music. ●

THE PROMS ON BBC RADIO 3

- Every Prom broadcast live (available on digital radio, via TV, mobile, laptop and tablet, as well as on 90–93FM)
- Many Proms repeated during *Afternoon on 3* (weekdays, 2.00pm) throughout the season, plus a series of repeats over the Christmas period
- Proms-related programmes throughout the season, including *In Tune* (weekdays, 4.30pm), *Record Review* (Saturdays, 9.00am) and *Composer of the Week* (weekdays, 12.00pm & 6.30pm)
- *Twenty Minutes* – related interval features exploring themes of the concert
- Proms Extra – coverage of pre-Prom talks given by Radio 3 presenters and other experts
- Catch up for 30 days at bbc.co.uk/proms

THE PROMS ON TV

- Broadcasts on Friday and Sunday on BBC Four throughout the season and on Saturdays on BBC Two during the Olympic Games
- Seven Friday-night broadcasts direct from the Royal Albert Hall throughout the season
- *Proms Extra* on BBC Two – hosted by Katie Derham every Saturday night during the season
- A series of five consecutive weekday-evening broadcasts on BBC Four in the week following the Olympic Games (22–26 August)
- A further four Proms filmed for viewing exclusively online and on BBC iPlayer
- Catch up for 30 days at bbc.co.uk/proms

THE PROMS ONLINE AND ON MOBILE

- Listen to every Prom in HD Sound and catch up for 30 days at bbc.co.uk/proms
- Watch video of televised works, listen to preview clips and link to tickets for Proms concerts
- Explore Proms performances by composer or artist
- Discover playlists from our experts or build your own and play in your favourite music-streaming service
- Go deeper into the music with a selection of programmes and podcasts
- Delve into specially written features, illustrated with audio and video
- Download programmes and concerts on the BBC iPlayer and iPlayer Radio apps and enjoy the Proms whenever and wherever you want

STAY INFORMED facebook.com/theproms @bbcproms (#bbcproms) or sign up for our newsletter: bbc.co.uk/proms

PIERINO

37 Thurloe Place, London SW7 2HP
Tel:0207 581 3770

Monday to Saturday
12 noon – 11.30pm

Sunday
12 noon – 11pm

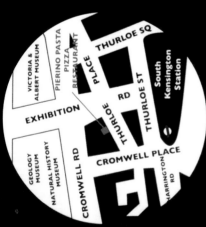

Prompt service guarenteed for you to be in time for the performance

We are within walking distance of the Royal Albert Hall, near South Kensington tube station.

You are welcome before and after the performance.

EXPERIENCE OF SERVING GENUINE ITALAN FOOD AND FOR HOME-MADE PASTA AND THE BEST PIZZA IN LONDON

40 YEARS

CONCERT LISTINGS

PROMS CONCERTS

Full details of all the 2016 BBC Proms concerts are in this section
(pages 112–149)

PROMS EXTRA

Look out, too, for the complementary series of free
Proms Extra events: find out more about the music through
lively introductions, or join in with workshops for all the family
(see also pages 66–71)

BOOKING

ONLINE **bbc.co.uk/proms**
TELEPHONE **0845 401 5040**[†]

General booking opens at 9.00am on Saturday 7 May

Plan your Proms concert-going before tickets go on sale
by using the Proms Planner at bbc.co.uk/proms from 2.00pm
on Wednesday 13 April until midnight on Friday 6 May
For full booking and access information, see pages 150–163

PRICE CODES (A) ▸ (H)

Each concert at the Royal Albert Hall falls into one of eight price
bands, colour-coded for ease of reference
For a full list of prices and booking fees, see page 150–151

Please note: *concert start-times vary across the season – check before you book*

[†]*see page 152 for call-cost information*

FRIDAY 15 JULY

PROM 1
7.00pm–c9.15pm • Royal Albert Hall

PRICE BAND B *Seats £9.50 to £48 (plus booking fee*)*
WEEKEND PROMMING PASS *see page 155*

Tchaikovsky
Fantasy-Overture 'Romeo and Juliet'   20'

Elgar Cello Concerto in E minor   29'

INTERVAL

Prokofiev
Alexander Nevsky – cantata   41'

Sol Gabetta *cello*
Olga Borodina *mezzo-soprano*

BBC National Chorus of Wales
BBC Symphony Chorus
BBC Symphony Orchestra
Sakari Oramo *conductor*

Tchaikovsky's ravishing *Romeo and Juliet* overture launches our celebrations marking 400 years since the death of Shakespeare. Argentine soloist Sol Gabetta makes her Proms debut in Elgar's hauntingly lyrical Cello Concerto, the first in a series of works throwing a spotlight on the instrument. Prokofiev delivered a score of new directness and clarity for his friend Sergey Eisenstein's patriotic film *Alexander Nevsky*: the cantata he fashioned from it features the dramatic 'Battle on the Ice'. See 'Poet, Playwright, Muse', pages 18–23; 'No More Second Fiddle', pages 34–37; 'Russian Heroes', pages 44–47; 'Latin Leaders', pages 98–99.

RADIO *Live on BBC Radio 3*
TV *First half on BBC Two, second half on BBC Four this evening*
ONLINE *Listen, watch and catch up at bbc.co.uk/proms*

SPOTLIGHT ON...
Sol Gabetta • Prom 1

'I truly love the Elgar Cello Concerto,' says Sol Gabetta. 'It's really an honour for me to play it at the First Night of the Proms, with an audience who knows the composer better than anyone else in the world.'

'I learnt the piece when I was 19,' explains the Argentine cellist, who will be making her Proms debut with the BBC Symphony Orchestra and Sakari Oramo for the first time here. 'At the time I wasn't quite sure how to approach it, because I couldn't identify with it easily.' The famous 1965 recording by Jacqueline du Pré is so well-known that it makes its very challenging for a young musician to find their own, personal interpretation of the work. 'It's very hard for a young musician to live up to it and to make something individual out of the music,' Gabetta explains. 'But I think now I've found the Elgar in me: I tried to be more sensitive to the inner expression and develop the intimate part of the music.'

Completed in 1919, the Cello Concerto was Elgar's last important piece. 'It's excellently composed for the cello,' says Gabetta. 'It's not a battle with the orchestra, but a dialogue. In the end the orchestra leaves me by myself with all the harmonies of sorrow. I think that what Elgar wants to tell us is that, even when we have friends, we are born and die alone and so we have to live our lives alone.'

SATURDAY 16 JULY

PROM 2
7.30pm–c9.45pm • Royal Albert Hall

PRICE BAND D *Seats £18 to £68 (plus booking fee*)*
WEEKEND PROMMING PASS *see page 155*

Mussorgsky Boris Godunov
(original version, 1869)   121'
(concert performance; sung in Russian)

Cast to include:
Bryn Terfel *Boris Godunov*
Benjamin Knight *Fyodor*
Vlada Borovko *Xenia*
John Graham-Hall *Shuisky*
Kostas Smoriginas *Shchelkalov*
Ain Anger *Pimen*
David Butt Philip *Grigory (Pretender Dmitry)*
Andrii Goniukov *Varlaam*
Harry Nicoll *Missail*
Rebecca de Pont Davies *Innkeeper*
Andrew Tortise *Yurodivy (Holy Fool)*

Royal Opera Chorus
Orchestra of the Royal Opera House
Sir Antonio Pappano *conductor*

There will be no interval

Modest Mussorgsky created music of white-hot inspiration in his operatic masterpiece *Boris Godunov*, which tells of a Tsar hounded by fear, danger and intrigue. Bryn Terfel leads an illustrious cast. See 'Russian Heroes', pages 44–47.

RADIO *Live on BBC Radio 3*
ONLINE *Listen and catch up at bbc.co.uk/proms*

PROMS EXTRA
12.30pm–3.30pm • Imperial College Union Join Mary King and the BBC Singers to sing excerpts from Mussorgsky's Boris Godunov. Experience in sight-reading or a knowledge of the piece is an advantage but not essential. Suitable for ages 16-plus. See pages 66–71 for details

5.15pm–6.30pm • Imperial College Union Proms Lecture: Four years after the spectacular opening of the London Olympics, writer of the Opening Ceremony, Frank Cottrell-Boyce, reflects on the cultural legacy of the Games, the importance of the arts in education and their wider influence on society. Edited version broadcast on BBC Radio 3 after tonight's Prom

SUNDAY 17 JULY

PROM 3
7.00pm–c9.30pm • Royal Albert Hall

PRICE BAND B *Seats £9.50 to £48 (plus booking fee*)*
WEEKEND PROMMING PASS *see page 155*

Mozart Exsultate, jubilate   *14'*

Haydn Mass in Time of War
('Paukenmesse')   *42'*

INTERVAL

Fauré
Pavane (choral version)   *7'*
Cantique de Jean Racine   *6'*
Requiem   *36'*

Lucy Crowe *soprano*
Paula Murrihy *mezzo-soprano*
Robin Tritschler *tenor*
Roderick Williams *baritone*

Choir of King's College, Cambridge
Orchestra of the Age of Enlightenment
Stephen Cleobury *conductor*

In a Prom of choral classics the Choir of King's College, Cambridge, follows intricate sacred works by Mozart and Haydn with the radiant serenity of Fauré, whose *Requiem* radiates stillness and spirituality. The King's choristers are joined by leading vocal soloists as well as the period instruments of the Orchestra of the Age of Enlightenment.

RADIO *Live on BBC Radio 3*
TV *Broadcast on BBC Four this evening*
ONLINE *Listen, watch and catch up at bbc.co.uk/proms*

PROMS EXTRA
2.30pm–5.30pm • Royal Albert Hall Join Mary King and the BBC Singers to sing excerpts from Fauré's *Requiem* with musicians from the Orchestra of the Age of Enlightenment. Experience in sight-reading or a knowledge of the piece is an advantage but not essential. *Suitable for ages 16-plus. See pages 66–71 for details*

5.00pm–5.30pm • Imperial College Union Tom Service presents a live edition of BBC Radio 3's *The Listening Service*, exploring the way music takes us to altered states of mind and spirit. *Tickets available from BBC Studio Audiences: bbc.co.uk/showsandtours/shows. Broadcast live on BBC Radio 3*

MONDAY 18 JULY

PROMS CHAMBER MUSIC 1
1.00pm–2.00pm • Cadogan Hall

Seats £12/£14 (plus booking fee*)

PAUL LEWIS

Debussy Cello Sonata   *13'*
Dutilleux Ainsi la nuit   *15'*
Mozart
Piano Concerto No. 12 in A major, K414 *25'*

Paul Lewis *piano*
Bjørg Lewis *cello*
Vertavo Quartet

There will be no interval

Paul Lewis joins his regular partners the Vertavo Quartet for the first of the season's Proms Chamber Music concerts. They begin with music from France: Debussy's Symbolist Cello Sonata and one of the most important string quartets of the 20th century, Henri Dutilleux's exploration of sound constructed on a single chord, *Ainsi la nuit*. To end, all five musicians are united for the quintet arrangement of Mozart's Piano Concerto No. 12, the jewel among his landmark concertos from the spring of 1782 and a work of rare intimacy, lightness and charm. *See 'The Power of Enchantment', pages 54–57.*

RADIO *Live on BBC Radio 3*
ONLINE *Listen and catch up at bbc.co.uk/proms*

MONDAY 18 JULY

PROM 4
7.30pm–c10.05pm • Royal Albert Hall

PRICE BAND C *Seats £14 to £58 (plus booking fee*)*

Ravel Boléro   *16'*
Rachmaninov
Piano Concerto No. 3 in D minor   *42'*

INTERVAL

Ustvolskaya Symphony No. 3,
'Jesus Messiah, Save Us!'   *14'*
R. Strauss Der Rosenkavalier – suite *25'*

Behzod Abduraimov *piano*
Munich Philharmonic Orchestra
Valery Gergiev *conductor*

Valery Gergiev and his Munich Philharmonic Orchestra open with Ravel's hypnotic *Boléro* and close with a suite from Richard Strauss's waltz-filled opera *Der Rosenkavalier*. In between, Galina Ustvolskaya's Symphony No. 3 pleads for redemption on raw brass and winds. Young Uzbek pianist Behzod Abduraimov – winner of the 2009 London International Piano Competition – is the soloist in Rachmaninov's soaring Piano Concerto No. 3.

RADIO *Live on BBC Radio 3*
TV *Recorded for broadcast on BBC Two on 20 August*
ONLINE *Listen, watch and catch up at bbc.co.uk/proms*

PROMS EXTRA
5.45pm–6.30pm • Imperial College Union (Dining Hall)
Join professional musicians for a family-friendly introduction to tonight's Prom. Bring your instrument and join in! *Suitable for all the family (ages 7-plus). See pages 66–71 for details*

5.45pm–6.30pm • Imperial College Union (Concert Hall)
Marking the bicentenary of Charlotte Brontë's birth, her biographer Claire Harman and Yorkshire-born novelist and author of *Chocolat* Joanne Harris discuss her life and work. *Edited version broadcast on BBC Radio 3 during tonight's interval*

TUESDAY 19 JULY

PROM 5
6.30pm–c8.15pm • Royal Albert Hall

PRICE BAND **A** *Seats £7.50 to £38 (plus booking fee*)*

GIANANDREA NOSEDA

Beethoven Missa solemnis   90'

Camilla Nylund *soprano*
Birgit Remmert *mezzo-soprano*
Stuart Skelton *tenor*
Hanno Müller-Brachmann *bass*

Hallé Choir
Manchester Chamber Choir
BBC Philharmonic
Gianandrea Noseda *conductor*

There will be no interval

In 1819 Ludwig van Beethoven was stirred by a new creative energy. Sketched over the next four years, on specially enlarged sheets of paper, was the work Beethoven himself came to admire above all others: his grand solemn mass, the *Missa solemnis*. Using every means of musical imagery available, Beethoven demonstrated his supreme mastery of the orchestral-choral model in this musical glimpse of heaven. The BBC Philharmonic, along with the Hallé Choir and Manchester Chamber Choir, bring Beethoven's vision to life under the orchestra's dynamic Conductor Laureate, Gianandra Noseda, recently named Music Director Designate of Washington's National Symphony Orchestra.

RADIO *Live on BBC Radio 3*
ONLINE *Listen and catch up at bbc.co.uk/proms*

PROMS EXTRA
4.45pm–5.30pm • Imperial College Union Ahead of tonight's performance of Beethoven's *Missa solemnis*, this first in a series of archive film screenings features Myra Hess's 1954 Celebrity Recital, in which she performs Bach (including *Jesu, joy of man's desiring*), and Beethoven's Piano Sonata in A flat major, Op. 110.

TUESDAY 19 JULY

PROM 6
10.15pm–c11.30pm • Royal Albert Hall

PRICE BAND **E** *Seats £7.50 to £25 (plus booking fee*)*

YOLANDA BROWN

GOSPEL PROM

Artists to include:
Israel J. Allen *singer*
Tehila Daniel *singer*
Dawn Thomas Wallace *singer*
YolanDa Brown *saxophone*
Niji Adeleye *keyboards/MD*

London Adventist Chorale
London Community Gospel Choir
Muyiwa & Riversongz
Noel Robinson & Nu Image
V9 Collective
Volney Morgan & New-Ye
University Gospel Choir of the Year Mass Choir
Karen Gibson *conductor*

There will be no interval

Following the success of the first ever Gospel Prom in 2013, a selection of handpicked singers from leading gospel groups come together to form an elite gospel 'superchoir' at the Royal Albert Hall. A late-night celebration featuring original material alongside traditional gospel classics and arrangements – plus a sprinkling of esteemed special guests.

RADIO *Live on BBC Radio 3*
TV/iPLAYER *Watch live at bbc.co.uk/proms*
ONLINE *Listen, watch and catch up at bbc.co.uk/proms*

WEDNESDAY 20 JULY

PROM 7
7.30pm–c9.20pm • Royal Albert Hall

PRICE BAND **A** *Seats £7.50 to £38 (plus booking fee*)*

JULIE FUCHS

Fauré Shylock   19'
Stravinsky Pulcinella – suite   23'

INTERVAL

Poulenc Stabat mater   30'

Julie Fuchs *soprano*
Julien Behr *tenor*

BBC Singers
BBC Symphony Orchestra
Marc Minkowski *conductor*

Paris was at the centre of the quest for new clarity and order in music around the start of the 20th century, and tonight's Prom presents some of the most delicious fruits of that quest. Our Shakespeare anniversary celebrations continue with a suite drawn from Fauré's incidental music for *The Merchant of Venice*. In his ballet score *Pulcinella*, Stravinsky dusted down Baroque melodies then believed to be by Pergolesi, lending them an ear-teasing bite. Spare simplicity and urbane wit usually meet in the works of Poulenc; but in his *Stabat mater* – a portrait of the mother of Christ beholding her crucified son – Poulenc finds a mode of disarming tenderness and contemplation. See 'Poet, Playwright, Muse', pages 18–23.

RADIO *Live on BBC Radio 3*
ONLINE *Listen and catch up at bbc.co.uk/proms*

PROMS EXTRA
5.45pm–6.30pm • Imperial College Union
Composer, director and translator Jeremy Sams introduces Poulenc's *Stabat mater*.
Edited version broadcast on BBC Radio 3 during tonight's interval

THURSDAY 21 JULY

PROM 8
7.30pm–c9.45pm • Royal Albert Hall

PRICE BAND D *Seats £18 to £68 (plus booking fee*)*

KATIE DERHAM

STRICTLY PROM

Katie Derham *presenter/dancer*

Joanne Clifton *dancer*
Karen Clifton *dancer*
Kevin Clifton *dancer*
Janette Manrara *dancer*
Giovanni Pernice *dancer*
Aljaž Skorjanec *dancer*

BBC Concert Orchestra
Gavin Sutherland *conductor*

Katie Derham dons her dance shoes and ball gown once more, joined by some of your favourite professionals from *Strictly Come Dancing*, who will whisk us from Vienna to Latin America and back in the company of the BBC Concert Orchestra and English National Ballet Music Director Gavin Sutherland. If you've ever wanted to know the difference between an English and Viennese waltz, or how classical composers have approached the Charleston and the tango, this is the Prom for you.

RADIO *Live on BBC Radio 3; recorded for future broadcast on BBC Radio 2*
TV *Recorded for broadcast on BBC Four on 22 July*
ONLINE *Listen, watch and catch up at bbc.co.uk/proms*

PROMS EXTRA

5.45pm–6.30pm • Imperial College Union Join Stephanie Jordan, Dance Research Professor at the University of Roehampton, for an introduction to tonight's Strictly Prom.
Edited version broadcast on BBC Radio 3 during tonight's interval

c10.00pm–c11.00pm • Elgar Room, Royal Albert Hall
Georgia Mann-Smith presents informal late-night music and poetry featuring emerging UK talent.
For details see bbc.co.uk/proms

FRIDAY 22 JULY

PROM 9
7.30pm–c9.40pm • Royal Albert Hall

PRICE BAND A *Seats £7.50 to £38 (plus booking fee*)*
WEEKEND PROMMING PASS *see page 155*

ROSA FEOLA

Mozart
Symphony No. 39 in E flat major, K543   *29'*

Mendelssohn Concert aria 'Infelice'   *13'*

INTERVAL

Mozart
Concert aria 'Ah, lo previdi', K272   *13'*

Mendelssohn
Symphony No. 4 in A major, 'Italian'   *27'*

Rosa Feola *soprano*

Le Cercle de l'Harmonie
Jérémie Rhorer *conductor*

Jérémie Rhorer's energetic period-instrument ensemble makes its Proms debut along with fast-rising soprano Rosa Feola. The orchestra opens with Mozart's vigorous Symphony No. 39, the first of the composer's final trilogy. Just like Mozart, Mendelssohn had an uncanny way of balancing head and heart in complex musical arguments, as heard in the thrusting brilliance of his Fourth Symphony, the 'Italian', tinged with poetry and romance.

RADIO *Live on BBC Radio 3*
ONLINE *Listen and catch up at bbc.co.uk/proms*

PROMS EXTRA

5.45pm–6.30pm • Imperial College Union This year marks the centenary of the death of the great American writer Henry James, who visited and fell in love with Italy at the age of 26. As this evening's Prom features Mendelssohn's 'Italian' Symphony, novelist and Henry James expert Philip Hensher takes the opportunity to reflect on his writing.
Edited version broadcast on BBC Radio 3 during tonight's interval

SPOTLIGHT ON...

Jérémie Rhorer • Prom 9

French conductor Jérémie Rhorer makes his BBC Proms debut, conducting Le Cercle de l'Harmonie, the period-instrument ensemble he founded in 2005, in works by Mozart and Mendelssohn. For him, these two composers almost represent different stages in a single tradition. 'There's a very natural development from the Classical style of Haydn and Mozart right through to the symphonies of Brahms,' he explains. 'For me, the big break really only came with Richard Strauss. And both Mozart's and Mendelssohn's music seem effortless, almost as if you can't see the art – that's one of the highest achievements in all music.'

Rhorer is a successful composer as well – he's just finished a Cello Concerto and one for piano is in the pipeline. He feels his perspective as a creator of new music is crucial when conducting works by others. 'I want it to be as though I'm writing the score as I'm conducting it, almost as if it becomes my own music. I've been very influenced in this sense by Leonard Bernstein conducting Mahler.'

With CD collaborations with eminent singers Diana Damrau and Philippe Jaroussky under his belt, Rhorer has achieved a lot in Le Cercle de l'Harmonie's decade of existence, but he feels his Proms performance will be something special: 'Everybody has the right to great music, however educated or rich they are. I think the Proms is one of the only festivals that's the incarnation of that, and I have a huge admiration for it.'

CONCERT LISTINGS

SATURDAY 23 JULY

PROM 10
11.00am–c1.00pm • Royal Albert Hall

PRICE BAND **H** *Seats £7.50 to £20 (plus booking fee*)*

TEN PIECES II PROM

Programme to include excerpts from:

J. S. Bach
Toccata and Fugue in D minor, BWV 565

Bernstein
Mambo (from *West Side Story*)

Bizet Habanera and Toreador Song
(from *Carmen*)

Anna Clyne Night Ferry

Haydn Trumpet Concerto in E flat
major – 3rd movement

Gabriel Prokofiev Concerto for
Turntables and Orchestra – 5th movement

Shostakovich Symphony No. 10
in E minor – 2nd movement

Vaughan Williams
The Lark Ascending

Verdi
Dies irae and Tuba mirum (from *Requiem*)

Wagner Ride of the Valkyries
(from *Die Walküre*)

Naomi Wilkinson *presenter*
Lemn Sissay *presenter*

DJ Mr Switch *turntables*
Matilda Lloyd *trumpet*
Esther Yoo *violin*
Wayne Marshall *organ*

Ten Pieces Choir
BBC Philharmonic
Alpesh Chauhan *conductor*

There will be one interval

Sign-interpreted performance: see page 162 for details

For concert description, see Prom 12

SPOTLIGHT ON...
Alpesh Chauhan • Prom 10

At the age of just 26, conductor Alpesh Chauhan
is particularly sensitive to the need to expose more
young people to classical music. 'As professional
musicians we all have a responsibility to build
new audiences,' he says, 'but as a young musician
I feel an even bigger duty to encourage young
people, some of whom aren't that much younger
than me, to try going to a concert, or watching or
listening to one.' It's no surprise, then, that he
jumped at the chance to be involved with the
BBC's Ten Pieces project for secondary schools.

As Assistant Conductor of the City of
Birmingham Symphony Orchestra since 2014 and
with his London Symphony Orchestra debut in
January next year, in which he conducts Brahms
and Richard Strauss, the fast-rising Chauhan gets
to explore lots of different repertoire. He applauds
the musical mix of the Ten Pieces: 'There's a wide
appeal in the selection, with music that speaks to
children from all backgrounds.' He's especially
excited about witnessing pupils' creative responses
to the Ten Pieces through compositions, dance,
digital art and performance poetry, some of which
will be showcased at the Ten Pieces II Proms.
'For me, the creative responses part is the most
important aspect of the initiative,' says Chauhan.
'By encouraging children to engage with the music
in this way, I think we will see a culturally richer
youth coming through – that's vital right now,
when there's so much pressure to focus on the
core subjects.'

SATURDAY 23 JULY

PROM 11
7.30pm–c9.45pm • Royal Albert Hall

PRICE BAND **A** *Seats £7.50 to £38 (plus booking fee*)*
WEEKEND PROMMING PASS *see page 155*

Wagner Die Walküre – final scene   30'

INTERVAL

Tippett A Child of Our Time   67'

Tamara Wilson *soprano*
Pamela Helen Stephen *mezzo-soprano*
Peter Hoare *tenor*
James Creswell *bass*

BBC National Chorus of Wales
BBC National Orchestra of Wales
Mark Wigglesworth *conductor*

As Europe slipped towards Fascism, Michael Tippett
felt solidarity with the downtrodden. Then, in 1938,
a young Polish Jew, whose parents had been
deported by the Nazis, shot a German diplomat in
Paris. Tippett had the central figure for his 'oratorio
of contemplation', *A Child of Our Time* – inspired by
Bach's Passions, Handel's *Messiah* and American
spirituals. Mark Wigglesworth also explores the
theme of parent–child relationships in the final
scene of Wagner's opera *Die Walküre*, culminating
in Wotan's poignant farewell to his daughter.

RADIO *Live on BBC Radio 3*
TV/iPLAYER *Tippett recorded for broadcast on BBC Four
on 24 July; watch Wagner online at bbc.co.uk/proms*
ONLINE *Listen, watch and catch up at bbc.co.uk/proms*

PROMS EXTRA

2.00pm–4.00pm • Imperial College Union Join Mary King and
members of the BBC Singers to sing the famous spirituals
from Tippett's *A Child of Our Time*. Suitable for ages 16-plus.
See pages 66–71 for details.

5.45pm–6.30pm • Imperial College Union Tippett expert
Oliver Soden introduces *A Child of Our Time* and discusses
the life and work of the composer. Edited version broadcast
on BBC Radio 3 during tonight's interval

SUNDAY 24 JULY

PROM 12
4.00pm–c6.00pm • Royal Albert Hall

PRICE BAND **H** *Seats £7.50 to £20 (plus booking fee*)*

DJ MR SWITCH

TEN PIECES II PROM

Naomi Wilkinson *presenter*
Lemn Sissay *presenter*

DJ Mr Switch *turntables*
Matilda Lloyd *trumpet*
Esther Yoo *violin*
Wayne Marshall *organ*

Ten Pieces Choir
BBC Philharmonic
Alpesh Chauhan *conductor*

There will be one interval

For programme, see Prom 10

After the success of last year's Ten Pieces Prom comes a new selection of classical essentials, this time aimed at secondary-school pupils. In the culmination of the Ten Pieces II project – which has taken classical music to schools across the UK – this Prom combines live performance with video animations. From the power of Wagner's 'Ride of the Valkyries' to the skills of DJ Mr Switch in Gabriel Prokofiev's Concerto for Turntables and Orchestra, the Ten Pieces II Prom also showcases creative responses from teenagers. See 'Ten Pieces II', pages 74–75.

RADIO *Live on BBC Radio 3, future broadcast on BBC Radio 2 (Prom 12)*
TV/iPLAYER *Recorded for future broadcast on CBBC. Watch live at bbc.co.uk/proms (Prom 12)*
ONLINE *Listen, watch and catch up at bbc.co.uk/proms*

PROMS EXTRA
1.00pm–3.00pm • Imperial College Union Proms Family Orchestra & Chorus: Join professional musicians to create your own music inspired by Ten Pieces II. Suitable for all the family (ages 7-plus). See pages 66–71 for details

---

SUNDAY 24 JULY

PROM 13
8.00pm–c9.35pm • Royal Albert Hall

PRICE BAND **B** *Seats £9.50 to £48 (plus booking fee*)*
WEEKEND PROMMING PASS *see page 155*

VLADIMIR JUROWSKI

Magnus Lindberg new work   c15'
BBC co-commission: world premiere

Beethoven Symphony No. 9
in D minor, 'Choral'   68'

Miah Persson *soprano*
Anna Stéphany *mezzo-soprano*
John Daszak *tenor*
Christopher Purves *bass*

London Philharmonic Chorus
London Philharmonic Orchestra
Vladimir Jurowski *conductor*

There will be no interval

Beethoven helped change the European musical landscape but in his final symphony he imagined the most startling transformation of all: from a brutal, joyless world to one of uplifting and embracing brotherhood. He did it by writing his most vivid music yet and employing – for the first time in a symphony – a chorus, proclaiming Friedrich Schiller's uplifting 'Ode to Joy'. Vladimir Jurowski returns to the Proms, opening with a new work from one of the finest orchestral craftsmen of our time, Magnus Lindberg. See 'New Music', pages 86–95.

RADIO *Live on BBC Radio 3*
ONLINE *Listen and catch up at bbc.co.uk/proms*

PROMS EXTRA
6.00pm–7.00pm • Imperial College Union Continuing our series of archive film screenings, pianists Solomon (1956) and Claudio Arrau (1960) perform works by Beethoven (Piano Sonatas in F minor, Op. 57, 'Appassionata', and in C minor, Op. 111) and an Impromptu by Schubert.

SPOTLIGHT ON...
Miah Persson • Prom 13

Proms audiences are used to encountering Beethoven's final symphony as a blast of high seriousness before the Last Night frolics. Not this year, when it turns up near the start of the festival, prefaced by a new work by Magnus Lindberg. It's all new, too, for Swedish soprano Miah Persson, who will be singing the lyrical quartet and heaven-storming finale for the very first time.

One of the great Mozartians of our age, Persson's elegantly gleaming soprano is surely ideal for a work where, in Wagner's words, 'the naive and the emotional are combined'. What will be the challenges be? 'As it's my first time singing the piece, I guess you'll have to ask me that after the concert!' But performing in the Royal Albert Hall itself holds no fears: 'I remember the first time I sang there, I thought to myself, "How on earth will I be heard in here?" But the amazing thing is that the acoustic is so great it has never actually presented any problems.' She joins the London Philharmonic Orchestra and Vladimir Jurowski, with whom she worked many times at Glyndebourne, when he was Music Director. 'I love working with Vladimir: he has a great understanding of singers.' Her happiest Proms memory is of the Glyndebourne *Così fan tutte* in 2006: 'We had sung 17 shows at the festival and ended the run in a semi-staged performance at the Proms. The fact that we knew the piece and each other so well made us relaxed and we could focus on having fun.'

MONDAY 25 JULY

PROMS CHAMBER MUSIC 2
1.00pm–c2.00pm • Cadogan Hall

Seats £12/£14 (plus booking fee*)

GUY JOHNSTON

Programme to include:

Brahms, arr. A. L. Christopherson
Hungarian Dance No. 5 in G minor   3'

Bach, arr. Robin Michael
Motet 'O Jesu Christ, meins Lebens Licht',
BWV 118   8'

Elgar, arr. David Johnstone
Enigma Variations – Nimrod   4'

Villa-Lobos Bachianas brasileiras
No. 5   13'

Julius Klengel
Hymnus for 12 cellos   7'

Golda Schultz _soprano_
**Guy Johnston, Emma Denton,
Benjamin Hughes, Su-a Lee,
Sarah McMahon, Robin Michael,
Brian O'Kane, Justin Pearson,
Pedro Silva, Victoria Simonsen,
Gabriella Swallow, Adi Tal** _cellos_

There will be no interval

As part of this season's celebration of the cello,
Guy Johnston gathers 11 of his cello-playing
friends for this celebration of the instrument in
all its expressive guises. From Bach to Brahms
via elegiac sounds from England and stomping
rhythms from Brazil, Johnston and his friends
demonstrate not only the cello's intense beauty
but also its versatility. See 'No More Second Fiddle',
pages 34–37; 'Latin Leaders', pages 98–99.

RADIO _Live on BBC Radio 3_
ONLINE _Listen and catch up at bbc.co.uk/proms_

MONDAY 25 JULY

PROM 14
7.00pm–c10.10pm • Royal Albert Hall

PRICE BAND C _Seats £14 to £58 (plus booking fee*)_

DANIELLE DE NIESE

Rossini The Barber of Seville   145'
(semi-staged; sung in Italian)

Danielle de Niese _Rosina_
Alessandro Corbelli _Dr Bartolo_
Taylor Stayton _Count Almaviva_
Björn Bürger _Figaro_
Christophoros Stamboglis _Don Basilio_
Janis Kelly _Berta_
Huw Montague Rendall _Fiorello_

Glyndebourne Festival Opera
London Philharmonic Orchestra
Enrique Mazzola _conductor_

There will be one interval

Glyndebourne makes its annual visit to the Proms,
bringing the ultimate comic opera. Rossini wrote
The Barber of Seville 200 years ago, reportedly in a
period of just three weeks, his head spinning with
the joy and wit he discovered in the story of the wily
hairdresser Figaro's amorous antics. The result is an
opera full of expectant fun but also oozing grace
and beauty. Leading soprano Danielle de Niese stars
as the young ward Rosina, eager to escape the
clutches of the elderly Count Almaviva in a highlight
of this summer's Proms Rossini focus. See 'Theatre in
the Blood', pages 24–27.

RADIO _Live on BBC Radio 3_
ONLINE _Listen and catch up at bbc.co.uk/proms_

PROMS EXTRA
5.15pm–6.00pm • Imperial College Union Ahead of
Glyndebourne's performance of _The Barber of Seville_,
New Generation Thinker Alun Withey and historian
Kathryn Hughes contemplate the role and politics of
hair-styling in 18th- and 19th-century Europe.
Edited version broadcast on BBC Radio 3 during tonight's interval

TUESDAY 26 JULY

PROM 15
7.30pm–c9.35pm • Royal Albert Hall

PRICE BAND A _Seats £7.50 to £38 (plus booking fee*)_

RAY CHEN

Tchaikovsky The Tempest   18'

Anthony Payne
Of Land, Sea and Sky   c20'
BBC commission: world premiere

INTERVAL

Bruch
Violin Concerto No. 1 in G minor   24'

Vaughan Williams
Toward the Unknown Region   12'

Ray Chen _violin_

BBC Symphony Chorus
BBC Symphony Orchestra
Sir Andrew Davis _conductor_

Vaughan Williams's _Toward the Unknown Region_
was his first large-scale masterpiece, setting the
visionary words of Walt Whitman. Sir Andrew
Davis also conducts Tchaikovsky's swashbuckling
The Tempest and the first performance of Anthony
Payne's _Of Land, Sea and Sky_. Bruch's radiant
First Violin Concerto completes the programme.
See 'Poet, Playwright, Muse', pages 18–23;
'New Music', pages 86–95.

RADIO _Live on BBC Radio 3_
ONLINE _Listen and catch up at bbc.co.uk/proms_

PROMS EXTRA
5.45pm–6.30pm • Imperial College Union Composers
in Conversation: Anthony Payne, who celebrates his
80th birthday this year, discusses his new work, _Of Land,
Sea and Sky_, and talks about his influences and inspirations;
with live performance and discussion.
Edited version broadcast on BBC Radio 3 after tonight's Prom

WEDNESDAY 27 JULY

PROM 16
7.00pm–c9.20pm • Royal Albert Hall

PRICE BAND Ⓐ *Seats £7.50 to £38 (plus booking fee*)*

CHLOË HANSLIP

Dukas
La Péri – Fanfare and Poème dansé   *20'*

Michael Berkeley Violin Concerto *c20'*
BBC commission: world premiere

INTERVAL

Prokofiev Romeo and Juliet – excerpts *48'*

Chloë Hanslip *violin*
BBC National Orchestra of Wales
Jac van Steen *conductor*

Paul Dukas's brief, intoxicating ballet *La Péri* opens tonight's Prom, before Chloë Hanslip gives the world premiere of a new Violin Concerto by Michael Berkeley. Jac van Steen conducts excerpts from one of the most dramatic and colourfully scored of all ballets, Prokofiev's *Romeo and Juliet*, a highlight of our series marking 400 years since the death of Shakespeare. See 'Poet, Playwright, Muse', pages 18–23; 'New Music', pages 86–95.

RADIO *Live on BBC Radio 3*
ONLINE *Listen and catch up at bbc.co.uk/proms*

PROMS EXTRA
5.15pm–6.00pm • Imperial College Union (Dining Hall)
Join professional musicians for a family-friendly introduction to tonight's Prom. Bring your instrument and join in! *Suitable for all the family (age 7-plus). See pages 66–71 for details*

5.15pm–6.00pm • Imperial College Union (Concert Hall)
In the first of a series of talks about Shakespeare and aspects of professional life examined in his plays, Colonel Tim Collins OBE discusses the depiction of soldiers and war in Shakespeare's work.
Edited version broadcast on BBC Radio 3 during tonight's interval

THURSDAY 28 JULY

PROM 17
7.30pm–c9.50pm • Royal Albert Hall

PRICE BAND Ⓑ *Seats £9.50 to £48 (plus booking fee*)*

ROBERT LEVIN

Berlioz
Beatrice and Benedict – overture   *8'*

Beethoven
Piano Concerto No. 4 in G major   *34'*

INTERVAL

Brahms Symphony No. 1 in C minor *47'*

Robert Levin *piano*
Stuttgart Radio Symphony Orchestra (SWR)
Sir Roger Norrington *conductor*

New sounds always emerge from Sir Roger Norrington's historically informed adventures with his old friends from Stuttgart. Tonight he turns his attention to the joyous overture from Berlioz's Shakespearean comedy *Beatrice and Benedict* and two works central to the Austro-German tradition: Beethoven's Fourth Piano Concerto and Brahms's First Symphony. See 'Poet, Playwright, Muse', pages 18–23.

RADIO *Live on BBC Radio 3*
ONLINE *Listen and catch up at bbc.co.uk/proms*

PROMS EXTRA
5.45pm–6.30pm • Imperial College Union
In the second talk about Shakespeare and aspects of professional life examined in his plays, the Rt Revd and Rt Hon. Richard Chartres, Bishop of London, discusses the place of religion in Shakespeare's works.
Edited version broadcast on BBC Radio 3 during tonight's interval

c10.00pm–c11.00pm • Elgar Room, Royal Albert Hall
Georgia Mann-Smith presents informal late-night music and poetry featuring emerging UK talent.
For details see bbc.co.uk/proms

SPOTLIGHT ON…

Sir Roger Norrington • Prom 17

Sir Roger Norrington feels he owes a great deal to the Stuttgart Radio Symphony Orchestra, where he was principal conductor for 13 years: 'Before I began there, I had only really conducted chamber orchestras in terms of historically informed performance. It showed me that a big symphony orchestra could take on the style and play with 'pure' tone – without vibrato. I took that to all the big symphony orchestras after that. It's been revelatory.' He's delighted to be opening this Prom with one of Berlioz's Shakespearean overtures, to *Beatrice and Benedict*: 'It's very charming, very tricky – and ends in a riot of good humour. There's nothing quite like Berlioz's passionate response to Shakespeare: which other composer actually married the first Juliet they saw – in this case actress Harriet Smithson?'

Robert Levin is the soloist in Beethoven's Piano Concerto No. 4; he and Norrington have been friends for 30 years. 'He's a consummate improviser,' says the conductor, 'which always makes performing a concerto with him so exciting. Sometimes we've done four performances in a row and every cadenza he conjures up is different.' Norrington 'adores' Brahms's First Symphony, which concludes the Prom: 'In Brahms's time it was normal for this to be performed with only eight first violins. We have 16, so we are doubling the winds to keep everything in proportion: it sounds wonderful to have that rich wind chorale in the last movement's sublime melody.'

FRIDAY 29 JULY

PROM 18
7.00pm–c8.55pm • Royal Albert Hall

PRICE BAND C *Seats £14 to £58 (plus booking fee*)*
WEEKEND PROMMING PASS *see page 155*

SARAH CONNOLLY

Mahler Symphony No. 3 in D minor   *101'*

Sarah Connolly *mezzo-soprano*

Eltham College Boys' Choir
London Symphony Chorus
(women's voices)
London Symphony Orchestra
Bernard Haitink *conductor*

There will be no interval

On the shores of the Attersee in Upper Austria, the hut still stands in which Gustav Mahler set about creating one of the most overwhelming visions of nature in all art. The composer's Third Symphony harnessed the expanse that surrounded him. Horns bray and trombones growl in the face of nature's primeval power; human voices move from grief to hope before, as Mahler declared, 'nature in its totality rings and resounds'. In the 50th-anniversary year of his first appearance at the Proms, Bernard Haitink conducts Mahler's almighty nature symphony. See 'Golden Record', pages 40–43.

RADIO *Live on BBC Radio 3*
TV *Broadcast on BBC Four this evening*
ONLINE *Listen, watch and catch up at bbc.co.uk/proms*

PROMS EXTRA
4.50pm–6.00pm • Imperial College Union In the 50th-anniversary year of Bernard Haitink's first appearance at the Proms, join us for a screening of his 1987 Prom with the BBC Symphony Orchestra, featuring Ravel's *Shéhérazade* with Felicity Lott and Stravinsky's *Petrushka*.

FRIDAY 29 JULY

PROM 19
10.15pm–c11.45pm • Royal Albert Hall

PRICE BAND F *Seats £10 to £35 (plus booking fee*)*
WEEKEND PROMMING PASS *see page 155*

DAVID BOWIE

DAVID BOWIE PROM

s t a r g a z e
André de Ridder *conductor*

There will be no interval

A celebration and reinterpretation of the music of David Bowie with the Berlin-based, genre-defying musicians' collective s t a r g a z e and its Artistic Director André de Ridder. They are joined by guest singers and collaborators – including Jherek Bischoff and Amanda Palmer – to re-imagine the Bowie catalogue with fresh settings of classic works.

RADIO *Live on BBC Radio 3, future broadcast on BBC Radio 6 Music*
TV *Broadcast on BBC Four this evening*
ONLINE *Listen, watch and catch up at bbc.co.uk/proms*

SATURDAY 30 JULY

PROM 20
7.30pm–c9.20pm • Royal Albert Hall

PRICE BAND B *Seats £9.50 to £48 (plus booking fee*)*
WEEKEND PROMMING PASS *see page 155*

SIR JOHN ELIOT GARDINER

Berlioz Romeo and Juliet   *95'*
(sung in French)

Julie Boulianne *mezzo-soprano*
Jean-Paul Fouchécourt *tenor*
Laurent Naouri *bass*

Monteverdi Choir
National Youth Choir of Scotland
Orchestre Révolutionnaire et
Romantique
Sir John Eliot Gardiner *conductor*

There will be no interval

When Hector Berlioz got his first taste of Shakespeare in 1827, he not only fell for 'the whole heaven of art' in the Bard's verse, he also fell madly in love with the actress Harriet Smithson. Shakespeare inspired a string of works from this most literary and dramatic of composers, including the ardent choral symphony *Romeo and Juliet*. See 'Poet, Playwright, Muse', pages 18–23.

RADIO *Live on BBC Radio 3*
TV *Recorded for broadcast on BBC Four on 31 July*
ONLINE *Listen, watch and catch up at bbc.co.uk/proms*

PROMS EXTRA
12.30pm–3.30pm • Imperial College Union Join Mary King and members of the BBC Singers to sing excerpts from Berlioz's *Romeo and Juliet*. Experience in sight-reading or a knowledge of the piece is an advantage but not essential. Suitable for ages 16-plus. See pages 66–71 for details

6.00pm–6.30pm • Imperial College Union Ahead of the performance of Berlioz's *Romeo and Juliet*, readings of Shakespeare and his Elizabethan contemporaries. *Edited version broadcast on BBC Radio 3 during the interval of the 'Proms at…' matinee on 13 August (3.00pm)*

SPOTLIGHT ON...
Julie Boulianne • Prom 20

French-Canadian mezzo-soprano Julie Boulianne tickled audiences in Chabrier's frivolous sparkling comedy *L'étoile* at the Royal Opera House, Covent Garden, earlier this year. And it's with another idiosyncratic French masterpiece that she makes her BBC Proms debut. Berlioz's choral symphony *Romeo and Juliet* is more the composer's personal response to Shakespeare's great tragic love story than a straightforward retelling and Boulianne has a key role to play in it, singing the first movement's tender love song. 'It's a very delicate and sensual moment,' she says. 'I think the key is to let the powerful text guide you through this very simple yet inspired music. It's an idealistic point of view about love, its beauty, value and fragility. It doesn't form part of the plot, but I feel it gives the audience a moment of meditation to fully understand and feel the two lovers' story. It has to be delivered with heart and humility, so for me it's the perfect way to make my Proms debut.'

Quebec-born Boulianne has performed at opera houses and concert halls through North America and Europe, but she feels the Berlioz work has always been with her. 'I was lucky enough to be introduced to this unique piece in my very first year at McGill University in Montreal and it's been following me ever since. And, because I only sing in the first part, I get to sit and calmly enjoy the rest of the music in all its brilliant complexity.'

SUNDAY 31 JULY

PROM 21
3.45pm–c6.00pm • Royal Albert Hall

PRICE BAND Ⓐ *Seats £7.50 to £38 (plus booking fee*)*
WEEKEND PROMMING PASS *see page 155*

NICHOLAS COLLON

Wolfgang Rihm
Gejagte Form (revised version, 2002)   13'

R. Strauss Oboe Concerto   25'

INTERVAL

Mozart Symphony No. 41 in C major,
K551 'Jupiter'   33'

Tom Service *presenter*
François Leleux *oboe*

Aurora Orchestra
Nicholas Collon *conductor*

It's difficult to imagine how Mozart could have followed his final symphony, the 'Jupiter' – a work of such scale, majesty and intensity. Tom Service and Nicholas Collon unpick Mozart's continuous stream of joy and invention, allowing us to get under the skin of this great work, which the Aurora Orchestra plays from memory. Before it, one of the world's leading oboists, François Leleux, plays Strauss's twisting, singing Oboe Concerto – itself preceded by Wolfgang Rihm's *Hunted Form*, whose animal energy suggests a pursuit more physical than a search merely for musical structure.

RADIO *Live on BBC Radio 3*
TV/iPLAYER *Mozart recorded for broadcast on BBC Four on 23 August; watch Rihm and Strauss at bbc.co.uk/proms*
ONLINE *Listen, watch and catch up at bbc.co.uk/proms*

PROMS EXTRA
11.00am–1.00pm • **Imperial College Union** Proms Family Orchestra & Chorus – join professional musicians to create your own music inspired by this afternoon's Prom. Suitable for all the family (ages 7-plus). See pages 66–71 for details

SUNDAY 31 JULY

PROM 22
7.30pm–c9.35pm • Royal Albert Hall

PRICE BAND Ⓐ *Seats £7.50 to £38 (plus booking fee*)*
WEEKEND PROMMING PASS *see page 155*

VADIM GLUZMAN

Ravel Mother Goose – suite   16'

Lera Auerbach The Infant Minstrel and His Peculiar Menagerie   30'
BBC co-commission: UK premiere

INTERVAL

Debussy
King Lear – Fanfare d'ouverture;
Le sommeil de Lear   5'

La mer   23'

Vadim Gluzman *violin*

Crouch End Festival Chorus
BBC Symphony Orchestra
Edward Gardner *conductor*

A new choral-orchestral work by Russian-American composer Lera Auerbach is surrounded by Ravel's shimmering fairy-tale suite, Debussy's glinting portrait of the sea and – in this Shakespeare anniversary year – Debussy's aborted incidental music for *King Lear*. See 'Poet, Playwright, Muse', pages 18–23; 'New Music', pages 86–95.

RADIO *Live on BBC Radio 3*
ONLINE *Listen and catch up at bbc.co.uk/proms*

PROMS EXTRA
5.45pm–6.30pm • **Imperial College Union** Continuing our exploration of the ways in which Shakespeare portrayed aspects of professional life, Geoffrey Robertson QC talks about the law and lawyers, contending that Shakespeare must either have studied at the Inns of Court or have been close friends with those who did. *Edited version broadcast on BBC Radio 3 during tonight's interval*

MONDAY 1 AUGUST

PROMS CHAMBER MUSIC 3
1.00pm–c2.00pm • Cadogan Hall

Seats £12/£14 (plus booking fee*)

ALEXANDRE THARAUD

A SATIE CABARET

Alistair McGowan *actor*
Jean Delescluse *singer*
Alexandre Tharaud *piano*

There will be no interval

French pianist and Satie champion Alexandre Tharaud leads a cabaret of music and words celebrating one of the most curious and innovative composers of the 20th century. He is joined by actor and impressionist Alistair McGowan (author of both a radio play and a documentary inspired by the composer) for a lunchtime foray featuring extracts from Satie's witty *Memoirs of an Amnesiac*. Along the way we discover more about the composer of the solo-piano *Gnossiennes* and *Gymnopédies*: a committed eccentric who embraced Surrealism, invented the term 'furniture music' (later to become 'ambient music'), frequented Montmartre's bohemian Le Chat Noir cabaret club, became seduced by an esoteric strain of mystical Catholicism and for a period ate only food that was white in colour.

RADIO *Live on BBC Radio 3*
ONLINE *Listen and catch up at bbc.co.uk/proms*

SPOTLIGHT ON...

Alistair McGowan • PCM 3

With a documentary and a radio play on the eccentric French composer already under his belt (both of them for BBC Radio 4), comedian, impressionist and actor Alistair McGowan is fast becoming the go-to guy for all things Satie. 'His music is so beautifully pure and calm and romantic,' says McGowan, 'and it was really the man who interested me alongside the music. I see myself a lot in him.' As well as Satie's renowned eccentricities – his bizarre titles for his musical pieces (the famous *Three Pieces in the Shape of a Pear*, perhaps, or even *Desiccated Embryos*), or his seven identical yellow suits, one for each day of the week – it's the composer's humorous writings that have fascinated McGowan. 'He came out with some great one-liners, almost in the manner of Groucho Marx. He wrote these very jocular, often quite surreal pieces of, essentially, comedy – if I compared them with anyone, it would be with Spike Milligan's writing in its sense of the absurd.'

It's some of these writings that McGowan brings to this lunchtime music-and-speech Prom, in which he's joined by French pianist Alexandre Tharaud. 'To my knowledge, Satie only ever performed one of them – called "In praise of critics" – so I'll be one of the few people to have ever performed them.' It was Satie's piano music that got amateur pianist McGowan back into playing – didn't he feel tempted to perform any of the pieces himself? 'On a stage like this, at the Proms, live on the radio? No thank you!'

MONDAY 1 AUGUST

PROM 23
7.30pm–c9.45pm • Royal Albert Hall

PRICE BAND (A) *Seats £7.50 to £38 (plus booking fee*)*

JOHN STORGÅRDS

Jörg Widmann Armonica *UK premiere*		14'
Schumann Violin Concerto in D minor		30'

INTERVAL

Sibelius The Tempest – Prelude		8'
Nielsen Symphony No. 5		35'

Christa Schönfeldinger *glass harmonica*
Teodoro Anzellotti *accordion*
Thomas Zehetmair *violin*

BBC Philharmonic
John Storgårds *conductor*

John Storgårds was the first Finnish violinist to record Schumann's unusual Violin Concerto, but he now steps to the podium, making way for Austrian violinist Thomas Zehetmair. Surrounding Schumann's gem of a concerto are the first UK performance of Jörg Widmann's ethereal *Armonica*, the storm-tossed Prelude from Sibelius's eerie depiction of Shakespeare's island realm and Carl Nielsen's landmark symphonic vision of good's triumph over evil. See 'Poet, Playwright, Muse', pages 18–23; 'New Music', pages 86–95.

RADIO *Live on BBC Radio 3*
ONLINE *Listen and catch up at bbc.co.uk/proms*

PROMS EXTRA

5.45pm–6.30pm • Imperial College Union Veteran sailor Sir Robin Knox-Johnston, the first man to circumnavigate the world non-stop single-handedly, talks about the sea, shipwrecks and sea captains depicted in Shakespeare's plays. *Edited version broadcast on BBC Radio 3 during tonight's interval*

Marco Borggreve (Tharaud, Storgårds)

TUESDAY 2 AUGUST

PROM 24
7.30pm–c10.00pm • Royal Albert Hall

PRICE BAND Ⓐ *Seats £7.50 to £38 (plus booking fee*)*

JUANJO MENA

Ginastera Ollantay   *14'*
London premiere

Britten Piano Concerto   *30'*

INTERVAL

Schubert
Symphony No. 9 in C major, 'Great'   *60'*

Steven Osborne *piano*

BBC Philharmonic
Juanjo Mena *conductor*

In his bittersweet Piano Concerto, Britten set out to exploit the piano's 'enormous compass, percussive qualities and suitability for figuration'. The result is a true bravura piece whose razor-sharp edge conceals a gregarious smile. Alongside the first London performance of Alberto Ginastera's very Argentine view of the symphony orchestra comes the inexorable momentum of Schubert's most invigorating symphony, his 'Great' Ninth. See 'New Music', pages 86–95; 'Latin Leaders', pages 98–99.

RADIO *Live on BBC Radio 3*
ONLINE *Listen and catch up at bbc.co.uk/proms*

PROMS EXTRA

5.45pm–6.30pm • Imperial College Union (Dining Hall)
Join professional musicians for a family-friendly introduction to tonight's Prom. Bring your instrument and join in! *Suitable for all the family (ages 7-plus). See pages 66–71 for details*

5.45pm–6.30pm • Imperial College Union (Concert Hall)
Novelist Patricia Duncker and New Generation Thinker Clare Walker-Gore of Trinity College, Cambridge, discuss George Eliot, her travels in 19th-century Germany and the music she refers to in her novels and diaries.
Edited version broadcast on BBC Radio 3 during tonight's interval

---

WEDNESDAY 3 AUGUST

PROM 25
7.30pm–c9.50pm • Royal Albert Hall

PRICE BAND Ⓑ *Seats £9.50 to £48 (plus booking fee*)*

ALBAN GERHARDT

Dvořák Cello Concerto in B minor   *38'*

INTERVAL

Bartók Duke Bluebeard's Castle   *61'*

Alban Gerhardt *cello*
Ildikó Komlósi *Judith*
John Relyea *Duke Bluebeard*

Royal Philharmonic Orchestra
Charles Dutoit *conductor*

The gothic horror story of Duke Bluebeard prompted some of the most imaginative, descriptive and shocking music Bartók would write. With its huge orchestra, underpinned in this concert performance by the mighty Royal Albert Hall organ, Bartók's score speaks of the darkness of Bluebeard's vast castle and the cold-blooded murder of his six wives. Under Principal Conductor Charles Dutoit, the Royal Philharmonic Orchestra conjures up Bartók's unsettling realm after Dvořák's Cello Concerto, which the composer believed 'outstrips the other two concertos of mine'.

RADIO *Live on BBC Radio 3*
ONLINE *Listen and catch up at bbc.co.uk/proms*

PROMS EXTRA

5.45pm–6.30pm • Imperial College Union In an introduction to Bartók's *Duke Bluebeard's Castle*, musicologist Heather Wiebe discusses the story behind the music and the life and work of the Hungarian composer.
Edited version broadcast on BBC Radio 3 during tonight's interval

---

THURSDAY 4 AUGUST

PROM 26
7.30pm–c9.55pm • Royal Albert Hall

PRICE BAND Ⓐ *Seats £7.50 to £38 (plus booking fee*)*

OLIVER KNUSSEN

Brahms Piano Concerto No. 2
in B flat major   *50'*

INTERVAL

Reinbert de Leeuw
Der nächtliche Wanderer   *54'*
UK premiere

Peter Serkin *piano*

BBC Symphony Orchestra
Oliver Knussen *conductor*

When Brahms came to write his Second Piano Concerto more than two decades after his First, out went the confident swagger of a man in his prime and in came a feeling of intimacy and expectation. Oliver Knussen balances the Brahms with the far-flung world of *Der nächtliche Wanderer* ('The Night Wanderer') by Dutch composer and conductor Reinbert de Leeuw. This deftly coloured symphonic poem has been described as 'a bath of beauty' and 'a high-density monument in music'. See 'New Music', pages 86–95.

RADIO *Live on BBC Radio 3*
ONLINE *Listen and catch up at bbc.co.uk/proms*

PROMS EXTRA

6.00pm–6.30pm • Imperial College Union A literary accompaniment to tonight's Prom, with readings from some of the leading German Romantic poets who inspired Brahms, including E. T. A. Hoffmann, and Goethe's 'Wanderer's Night Songs'.
Edited version broadcast on BBC Radio 3 during tonight's interval

c10.00pm–c11.00pm • Elgar Room, Royal Albert Hall
Georgia Mann-Smith presents informal late-night music and poetry, featuring young talent. *For details see bbc.co.uk/proms*

FRIDAY 5 AUGUST

PROM 27
7.00pm–c9.05pm • Royal Albert Hall

PRICE BAND **A** *Seats £7.50 to £38 (plus booking fee*)*
WEEKEND PROMMING PASS *see page 155*

PEKKA KUUSISTO

Helen Grime Two Eardley Pictures –
1: Catterline in Winter   c8'
BBC commission: world premiere

Tchaikovsky
Violin Concerto in D major   33'

INTERVAL

Stravinsky Petrushka   35'

Pekka Kuusisto *violin*
BBC Scottish Symphony Orchestra
Thomas Dausgaard *conductor*

Tonight's Prom marks the first instalment of all three
of Stravinsky's landmark ballets for the Ballet Russes
company, all performed this weekend by Scottish
orchestras. In the vivid folk tale of a puppet springing
to life, Stravinsky had the starting point for his stylistic
breakthrough, *Petrushka*, a ballet that would depict
Russia with 'quick tempos, smells of Russian food,
sweat and glistening leather boots'. The first part
of a new work from major talent Helen Grime
(see *also Prom 30*) prefaces this concert's arrival in
Russia via all the despair, passion and determination
of Tchaikovsky's heart-rending Violin Concerto.
See 'New Music', pages 86–95.

RADIO *Live on BBC Radio 3*
TV *Broadcast on BBC Four this evening*
ONLINE *Listen, watch and catch up at bbc.co.uk/proms*

PROMS EXTRA
5.15pm–6.00pm • Imperial College Union Composers
in Conversation: Helen Grime introduces the first part
of her new two-part commission, *Two Eardley Pictures*,
and talks about her inspiration and ideas.
Edited version broadcast on BBC Radio 3 during tonight's interval

FRIDAY 5 AUGUST

PROM 28
10.15pm–c11.30pm • Royal Albert Hall

PRICE BAND **E** *Seats £7.50 to £25 (plus booking fee*)*
WEEKEND PROMMING PASS *see page 155*

IAIN BALLAMY

Iain Ballamy *saxophone*
Liane Carroll *piano/vocals*

**National Youth Jazz Orchestra
of Scotland**
Malcolm Edmonstone *piano*
Andrew Bain *conductor*

The weekend of Scottish ensembles continues
with a visit from the National Youth Jazz Orchestra
of Scotland, whose Late Night Prom marks the
Shakespeare anniversary with Duke Ellington's
jazz tribute to the Bard, *Such Sweet Thunder*. With
instruments taking the roles of actors, Ellington's
piece broke new ground when it appeared in 1957
as part of a 12-part Shakespeare-themed album,
and it still feels entirely fresh today. The NYJOS
welcomes back previous collaborators –
saxophonist Iain Ballamy performing some of his
compositions such as *All Men Amen* and *Floater*
along with pianist/vocalist Liane Carroll – to
perform a series of arrangements by Malcolm
Edmonstone, including songs made popular by
Frank Sinatra, The Beatles, Carole King and others.
See 'Poet, Playwright, Muse', pages 18–23.

RADIO *Live on BBC Radio 3*
ONLINE *Listen and catch up at bbc.co.uk/proms*

SPOTLIGHT ON...

Liane Carroll • Prom 28

After working and touring with the National
Youth Jazz Orchestra of Scotland during the
past four years, Liane Carroll is full of praise
for her young Proms collaborators: 'Not only
do they have an incredible respect for the music,
but they also have great respect for each other,
which is an excellent foundation for a long
career playing music.'

Carroll's own long career has seen her
performing all over the world, from her
home town of Hastings to Hawaii. Her regular
band is a trio in which she sings and plays piano,
so a date with a big band like the National
Youth Jazz Orchestra of Scotland is always
special. 'It'll be a treat to have the band behind
me, with its co-director Malcolm Edmonstone
at the piano, and just stand up and sing the
music,' she says. Edmonstone played piano
on Carroll's acclaimed 2015 album *Seaside*
and has arranged some of the songs from that
album for the Proms performance.

Carroll's excited too about performing alongside
the night's other guest artist, saxophonist Iain
Ballamy. 'Iain's a brilliant innovator,' she says.
'We've both been around quite a while, but I
think the older you get, the more you try to
learn. The day I don't want to learn, or struggle,
or find a bit more of my voice, is the day I give
up, get a dog and walk it. I don't want to do
that yet.'

SATURDAY 6 AUGUST
PROMS AT … THE CHAPEL, OLD ROYAL NAVAL COLLEGE, GREENWICH (see page 161) 3.00pm–c4.30pm

Seats £14 (plus booking fee*)/£6; for booking details, see pages 150–163

KATHRYN RUDGE

Rossini Petite messe solennelle 78'

Elizabeth Watts soprano
Kathryn Rudge mezzo-soprano
Peter Auty tenor
James Platt bass

Richard Pearce harmonium
Iain Farrington piano

BBC Singers
David Hill conductor

There will be no interval

'There is more faith in honest doubt,' Rossini once said. In his 'Little Solemn Mass' – famously neither little nor solemn – he somehow captured that feeling in music whose joy is tinged with grief and anxiety, amid vocal writing of purity and pungency. For this first 'Proms at …' matinee, in the stunning Old Chapel of the Old Royal Naval College, Greenwich, the BBC Singers and David Hill present the Proms premiere of what the composer called 'the last mortal sin of my old age'. See 'Theatre in the Blood', pages 24–27.

RADIO Live on BBC Radio 3
ONLINE Listen and catch up at bbc.co.uk/proms

SATURDAY 6 AUGUST
PROM 29
7.30pm–c10.00pm • Royal Albert Hall

PRICE BAND A Seats £7.50 to £38 (plus booking fee*)
WEEKEND PROMMING PASS see page 155

EDWARD GARDNER

Iris ter Schiphorst
Gravitational Waves 8'
BBC co-commission: London premiere

R. Strauss Also sprach Zarathustra 34'

INTERVAL

Holst The Planets 52'

including
Colin Matthews Pluto, the Renewer 7'

City of Birmingham Symphony Youth Chorus (women's voices)
National Youth Orchestra of Great Britain
Edward Gardner conductor

Film directors have reached for these works by Strauss and Holst in their attempts to explain the human condition against the infinite background of space. The depiction of astrological characters in The Planets, from the cheeky gameplay of Mercury to the shattering impact of Mars, could be made for the resonance of the Royal Albert Hall. The power of Strauss's Also sprach Zarathustra is no less cinematic. See 'New Music', pages 86–95.

RADIO Live on BBC Radio 3
TV/iPLAYER Watch live at bbc.co.uk/proms
ONLINE Listen, watch and catch up at bbc.co.uk/proms

PROMS EXTRA
5.45pm–6.30pm • Imperial College Union Ahead of Holst's The Planets, novelist Stephen Baxter examines the work of science-fiction writer H. G. Wells, born 150 years ago. He is joined by New Generation Thinker Sarah Dillon. Edited version broadcast on BBC Radio 3 during tonight's interval

SPOTLIGHT ON…
Millie Ashton, leader of the NYOGB • Prom 29

'Our annual Prom is the highlight of the National Youth Orchestra of Great Britain year,' says Millie Ashton, the violinist currently enjoying her first year leading this brilliant ensemble of young musicians. 'There's always a buzz from the moment you wake up on concert day. The whole experience is amazing, the best a teenage musician could ask for.'

This year, the NYO Prom brings together two large-scale masterpieces: Holst's The Planets and Strauss's Also sprach Zarathustra. 'I started learning the Strauss in January as there are some huge violin solos, which are a big deal for me,' explains Ashton. 'The NYO violin tutor told me to start learning early so that, by the time the Prom comes round, I will know them so well I won't have to worry about them. I'm so excited about it!' And how about the Holst? 'Some people in the orchestra will have played it before, but I haven't – because we're so young, many, like me, will be coming to this music for the first time.'

Everyone will be new to the first item on the programme, a Proms commission by the German composer Iris ter Schiphorst. 'We love bringing new pieces to life,' says Ashton. 'I hope Iris enjoys the team spirit of the group. We're the world's greatest orchestra of teenagers!'

SUNDAY 7 AUGUST

PROM 30
3.45pm–c6.10pm • Royal Albert Hall

PRICE BAND **A** *Seats £7.50 to £38 (plus booking fee*)*
WEEKEND PROMMING PASS *see page 155*

PAVEL KOLESNIKOV

Helen Grime Two Eardley Pictures –
2: Snow
BBC commission: world premiere   c8

Tchaikovsky
Piano Concerto No. 2 in G major   40'

INTERVAL

Stravinsky The Firebird   46'

Pavel Kolesnikov *piano*

National Youth Orchestra of Scotland
Ilan Volkov *conductor*

The National Youth Orchestra of Scotland frames
the turbulent and virtuosic Second Piano Concerto
by Tchaikovsky with the final part of Helen Grime's
new two-part work for orchestra (*see also Prom 27*)
and the second of this weekend's trio of Stravinsky
ballet scores. With *The Firebird* of 1910, Stravinsky
was immediately recognised as the most important
musical voice of the new century. His relentless
rhythmic drive and hypnotising orchestral colours
are heard to full advantage in a performance of the
complete ballet under the charismatic Ilan Volkov.
See 'New Music', pages 86–95.

RADIO *Live on BBC Radio 3*
ONLINE *Listen and catch up at bbc.co.uk/proms*

PROMS EXTRA
2.00pm–2.45pm • Imperial College Union Join professional
musicians for a family-friendly introduction to this afternoon's
Prom. Bring your instrument and join in! *Suitable for all the
family (ages 7-plus). See pages 66–71 for details*

SUNDAY 7 AUGUST

PROM 31
7.30pm–c9.45pm • Royal Albert Hall

PRICE BAND **A** *Seats £7.50 to £38 (plus booking fee*)*
WEEKEND PROMMING PASS *see page 155*

THOMAS DAUSGAARD

Prokofiev Scythian Suite   20'

Tchaikovsky Piano Concerto No. 1
in B flat minor (original version, 1879)   34'

INTERVAL

Stravinsky The Rite of Spring   34'

Kirill Gerstein *piano*

BBC Scottish Symphony Orchestra
Thomas Dausgaard *conductor*

The BBC Scottish Symphony Orchestra and its
Chief Conductor Thomas Dausgaard round off this
weekend's Stravinsky/Scottish series with the work
that changed music for ever. In *The Rite of Spring*
rhythm was shockingly prioritised over harmony
– and pounding, jagged, brutal rhythm at that. One
of *The Rite's* most impactful relatives is the *Scythian
Suite* by Stravinsky's compatriot Prokofiev, a blazing
orchestral canvas that forms the perfect foil to the
heartfelt beauty of Tchaikovsky's charming First
Piano Concerto, performed by Kirill Gerstein in
a new critical edition which, he says, 'allows us to
return to Tchaikovsky's original intentions'.

RADIO *Live on BBC Radio 3*
ONLINE *Listen and catch up at bbc.co.uk/proms*

PROMS EXTRA
5.45pm–6.30pm • Imperial College Union Stravinsky expert
Jonathan Cross examines *The Rite of Spring*.
Edited version broadcast on BBC Radio 3 during tonight's interval

SPOTLIGHT ON...

Kirill Gerstein • Prom 31

If you think you know how Tchaikovsky's First
Piano Concerto goes, think again. So says pianist
Kirill Gerstein, who is championing a new, rather
different edition of the famous concerto. It reveals
the 1879 version of the piece, which is the score
Tchaikovsky is known to have himself conducted.
The standard version in fact dates from after his
death. 'It's a big shock that something we're so
used to hearing is actually something that was
heavily edited posthumously,' explains Gerstein.
'The traditional bombastic as-loud-as-you-can,
drown-out-the-orchestra opening chords are
actually not what Tchaikovsky had in mind
at all. In fact those chords have a more lyrical
dynamic and they are partly arpeggiated.'

'All the differences paint a portrait of the piece
that's more musical, less purely athletic,' he says.
'It's closer to Schumann's spirit than to the
traditional Soviet bombast.' Gerstein will be
giving the first modern-day performance in the
UK of this edition, and there's a British
connection: 'It's likely that this version
incorporated suggestions by the pianist Edward
Dannreuther, one of the early exponents of the
concerto,' says Gerstein. 'He played the piece early
on in London's Crystal Palace in 1876.' Gerstein
has been the first to perform and record this new
edition of the concerto and he won't return to
the more familiar version. 'I would think that
it's musically and factually dishonest!' he says.
'But hopefully we will have started a trend.'

MONDAY 8 AUGUST

PROMS CHAMBER MUSIC 4
1.00pm–c2.00pm • Cadogan Hall

Seats £12/£14 (plus booking fee*)

HÅKAN HARDENBERGER

Tobias Broström Sputnik · 5'

Weill songs, including from 'The Threepenny Opera' and 'The Rise and Fall of the City of Mahagonny' · 20'

Kurt Schwertsik Adieu Satie – excerpts · 10'

HK Gruber Three MOB Pieces · 10'

Håkan Hardenberger *trumpet*
HK Gruber *voice*
John Constable *piano*
Mats Bergström *banjo/guitar*
Claudia Buder *accordion*

Academy of St Martin in the Fields

There will be no interval

The most intrepid of trumpeters, Håkan Hardenberger is joined by the Academy of St Martin in the Fields and some special friends for a celebration of the music of Kurt Weill and of proponents of the subversive and at times irreverent 'Third Viennese School', among them Kurt Schwertsik and HK Gruber, who appears as vocalist.

RADIO *Live on BBC Radio 3*
ONLINE *Listen and catch up at bbc.co.uk/proms*

MONDAY 8 AUGUST

PROM 32
7.30pm–c9.40pm • Royal Albert Hall

PRICE BAND Ⓐ *Seats £7.50 to £38 (plus booking fee*)*

ESA-PEKKA SALONEN

Schoenberg
A Survivor from Warsaw · 8'

Dutilleux The Shadows of Time · 30'

INTERVAL

Mahler Symphony No. 1 in D major · 53'

Simon Russell Beale *narrator*
Philharmonia Voices (men's voices)
Philharmonia Orchestra
Esa-Pekka Salonen *conductor*

Mahler's First Symphony isn't just the opening chapter of the composer's spiritual autobiography, it's also an awakening in itself. From hushed strings and woodwind cuckoos, it breaks into a forthright stride towards, eventually, a blazing affirmation of camaraderie and confidence. Esa-Pekka Salonen conducts the symphony here with his own Philharmonia Orchestra, following meditations on loss from Arnold Schoenberg and centenary composer Henri Dutilleux, whose The Shadows of Time was inspired by the diaries of Anne Frank and written to mark 50 years since the end of the Second World War. See 'The Power of Enchantment', pages 54–57.

RADIO *Live on BBC Radio 3*
ONLINE *Listen and catch up at bbc.co.uk/proms*

PROMS EXTRA
5.45pm–6.30pm • Imperial College Union Eva Schloss, stepsister of Anne Frank, reads from Anne's memoir and talks about the fate of Anne and other children during the Second World War, to whom Dutilleux's The Shadows of Time is dedicated'.
Edited version broadcast on BBC Radio 3 during tonight's interval

TUESDAY 9 AUGUST

PROM 33
7.30pm–c9.45pm • Royal Albert Hall

PRICE BAND Ⓐ *Seats £7.50 to £38 (plus booking fee*)*

JOHANNES MOSER

Mark Simpson Israfel · 12'
London premiere

Dutilleux
'Tout un monde lointain …' · 28'

INTERVAL

Elgar Symphony No. 1 in A flat major · 51'

Johannes Moser *cello*
BBC Philharmonic
Juanjo Mena *conductor*

In his First Symphony, unveiled in Manchester in 1911, Edward Elgar saw beyond the recession in which Britain was languishing to express a 'massive hope for the future'. The symphony's noble main tune appears fragile at first. But when it returns at the end, it's carried home by an ecstatic orchestra filled with a spirit of uplifting optimism. The BBC Philharmonic and its Chief Conductor also present the London premiere of a work by its Composer in Association Mark Simpson and the marriage of modernity and beauty that is Dutilleux's cello concerto 'Tout un monde lointain …'. See 'The Power of Enchantment', pages 54–57; 'New Music', pages 86–95.

RADIO *Live on BBC Radio 3*
ONLINE *Listen and catch up at bbc.co.uk/proms*

PROMS EXTRA
5.45pm–6.30pm • Imperial College Union Musicologist J. P. E. Harper-Scott introduces Elgar's First Symphony.
Edited version broadcast on BBC Radio 3 during tonight's interval

WEDNESDAY 10 AUGUST

PROM 34
7.30pm–c9.35pm • Royal Albert Hall

PRICE BAND Ⓐ *Seats £7.50 to £38 (plus booking fee*)*

Dutilleux
Timbres, espace, mouvement   20'

HK Gruber Busking   30'
London premiere

INTERVAL

Beethoven
Symphony No. 5 in C minor   35'

Håkan Hardenberger *trumpet*
Mats Bergström *banjo*
Claudia Buder *accordion*

BBC Symphony Orchestra
Sakari Oramo *conductor*

Two centuries on, Beethoven's Fifth Symphony has lost none of its shattering power. A tirade against destiny, it remains one of the most compelling yet perfect musical arguments ever created. Sakari Oramo conducts it here, after the pulsating drive of HK Gruber's *Busking*, performed by Håkan Hardenberger, the soloist for whom it was created. But, to start, music of pictorial delicacy: Henri Dutilleux's sonic reproduction of the cosmic, whirling effect of Van Gogh's painting *The Starry Night*. See 'The Power of Enchantment', pages 54–57; 'New Music', pages 86–95.

RADIO *Live on BBC Radio 3*
ONLINE *Listen and catch up at bbc.co.uk/proms*

PROMS EXTRA
5.45pm–6.30pm • Imperial College Union French music specialist Caroline Rae introduces Dutilleux's *Timbres, espace, mouvement* and discusses the life and work of the composer, whose centenary we celebrate this year. *Edited version broadcast on BBC Radio 3 during tonight's interval*

c9.45pm–c10.45pm • Elgar Room, Royal Albert Hall Georgia Mann-Smith presents informal late-night music and poetry featuring emerging UK talent. *For details see bbc.co.uk/proms*

SPOTLIGHT ON...
Håkan Hardenberger • Prom 34

Swedish trumpet virtuoso Håkan Hardenberger is not only back at the Proms for the third year in a row, but is also celebrating 30 years since his first appearance. 'I remember being quite nervous before one of my early Proms performances,' he says, 'but the conductor Elgar Howarth, whose house I was staying in, said, "Don't worry. It's just like a party." He was right, and that's how I always feel about the Proms: it's a party for music.'

The concerto he's bringing to the party this time, *Busking*, is HK Gruber's follow-up to the highly successful *Aerial*, a 1999 Proms commission which Hardenberger also premiered and has since has performed some 75 times. '*Aerial* is for a big orchestra, with huge soloistic challenges: lots of changes of instrument, mutes, taking the trumpet apart, even singing while playing,' says the trumpeter. 'When Gruber and I started talking about a second, chamber-orchestra concerto, I challenged him to write for just one trumpet, with no mutes or singing. He looked like a child who's had all his Christmas gifts taken away. "Can you at least start playing on the mouthpiece only?" he asked.'

As it turned out, the piece requires C and E flat trumpets, flugelhorn and mutes. 'Mr Gruber didn't abide by any of my rules,' jokes Hardenberger. 'The concerto, like *Aerial*, certainly has its challenges, but the gorgeous second movement has some of the most beautiful music for trumpet.'

THURSDAY 11 AUGUST

PROM 35
7.00pm–c8.55pm • Royal Albert Hall

PRICE BAND Ⓐ *Seats £7.50 to £38 (plus booking fee*)*

TAI MURRAY

Bartók Dance Suite   18'

Malcolm Hayes Violin Concerto   c24'
BBC commission: world premiere

INTERVAL

Dvořák Symphony No. 7 in D minor   35'

Tai Murray *violin*

BBC National Orchestra of Wales
Thomas Søndergård *conductor*

When the London Philharmonic Society asked Dvořák for a new symphony in 1884, the composer knew he had to deliver something special. In the resulting Seventh, the doubts and frustrations Dvořák experienced as a composer are defeated by music that triumphs compellingly over its own nervous energy, bursting into radiant brightness in its final bars. Tonight, Dvořák's most fascinating symphony is heard after Malcolm Hayes's new concerto, a work inspired by the mood and atmosphere of the Outer Hebrides, and performed by former BBC Radio 3 New Generation Artist Tai Murray. Bartók's colourful *Dance Suite*, featuring Hungarian and Arabic folk melodies, opens the concert. See 'New Music', pages 86–95.

RADIO *Live on BBC Radio 3*
ONLINE *Listen and catch up at bbc.co.uk/proms*

PROMS EXTRA
5.15pm–6.00pm • Imperial College Union Author and musicologist Jan Smaczny introduces Dvořák's Seventh Symphony and discusses the life and work of the composer. *Edited version broadcast on BBC Radio 3 during tonight's interval*

THURSDAY 11 AUGUST

PROM 36
10.15pm–c11.30pm • Royal Albert Hall

PRICE BAND (F) *Seats £10 to £35 (plus booking fee*)*

JULES BUCKLEY

JAMIE CULLUM PROM

with special guests, including emerging talent from BBC Music Introducing

Jamie Cullum *piano/vocals*

Roundhouse Choir
Heritage Orchestra
Jules Buckley *conductor*

Straddling the boundaries of jazz, pop and rock, Jamie Cullum returns for another Late Night Prom after his sell-out appearance in 2010. This time, backed by the Roundhouse Choir and Heritage Orchestra, he offers his own take on a collection of pop songs, in the spirit of The Song Society – Cullum's project to create fast and loose covers of favourite tracks. He brings the same approach of new discovery both to his use of the wide array of instruments available and to exploring the distinctive space of the Royal Albert Hall.

RADIO *Live on BBC Radio 3; recorded for future broadcast on BBC Radio 2*
TV *Recorded for broadcast on BBC Four on 26 August*
ONLINE *Listen, watch and catch up at bbc.co.uk/proms*

SPOTLIGHT ON...
Jamie Cullum • Prom 36

When UK jazz star Jamie Cullum made his BBC Proms debut back in 2010, he filled the Royal Albert Hall with feel-good tunes alongside crack crossover band the Heritage Orchestra. This year, however, he's planning something very different. 'The Proms is going to focus on songs – some of my own and some new and exciting interpretations,' he explains. 'Crucially, though, I'm going to try and use the space and the instrumentation available to me in an interesting way.'

Cullum is still finalising the fine details of his late-night gig, but he's taken inspiration for it from the venue itself. 'The Royal Albert Hall is one of those curious venues that can feel at once very intimate and then incredibly grand and open. I intend to exploit that unique quality in this concert.'

What role does he think jazz has in this eminent musical celebration? 'I hope we're at a stage now where artistic merit is judged beyond genres. I'm glad the Proms shines light on all areas of music.' And he's delighted to be able to bring his music to the diverse audience that the Proms attracts. 'You get an opportunity to play to people who might not necessarily have thought about coming to see you. All ages, all levels of musical knowledge, all with open minds – my favourite kind of audience.'

FRIDAY 12 AUGUST

PROM 37
7.30pm–c9.30pm • Royal Albert Hall

PRICE BAND (A) *Seats £7.50 to £38 (plus booking fee*)*
WEEKEND PROMMING PASS *see page 155*

Walton Partita   16'

Huw Watkins Cello Concerto   c25'
BBC commission: world premiere

INTERVAL

Webern Passacaglia   11'

Brahms Symphony No. 4 in E minor   39'

Paul Watkins *cello*

BBC National Orchestra of Wales
Thomas Søndergård *conductor*

Thomas Søndergård conducts his BBC National Orchestra of Wales in a Prom exploring the idea of the orchestral 'passacaglia' and some of the most delicious and subtle orchestral sonorities ever conjured. Brahms's fourth and final symphony feels like the composer's supreme orchestral achievement; its finale, a radiant passacaglia, is the summation of the composer's quest to wed discipline and emotion. After Walton's boisterous *Partita* comes the world premiere of the latest Proms cello concerto, a piece written by Huw Watkins and played by his brother. *See 'New Music', pages 86–95.*

RADIO *Live on BBC Radio 3*
ONLINE *Listen and catch up at bbc.co.uk/proms*

PROMS EXTRA
5.45pm–6.30pm • Imperial College Union Laura Tunbridge offers an insight into Brahms's Fourth Symphony in the context of the other works in tonight's programme.
Edited version broadcast on BBC Radio 3 during tonight's interval

Chris Christodoulou/BBC (Buckley); McVinn Etienne (Cullum)

10–12 AUGUST

SATURDAY 13 AUGUST
PROMS AT ... SAM WANAMAKER PLAYHOUSE, SHAKESPEARE'S GLOBE
(see page 161) 3.00pm–c5.00pm & 8.00pm–c10.00pm

Seats £14 (plus booking fee); for booking details, see pages 150–163*

SAMUEL BODEN

Shakespeare-themed works by Purcell, Blow, Locke and Draghi, including excerpts from music for 'Timon of Athens', 'The Fairy Queen' (after 'A Midsummer Night's Dream') and 'The Tempest'

Katherine Watson *soprano*
Samuel Bodsen *tenor*
Callum Thorpe *bass*

Arcangelo
Jonathan Cohen *harpsichord/organ/director*

There will be one interval

From one of London's biggest auditoria to one of its smallest – the Proms moves east for a celebration of Restoration theatre music at the intimate jewel-box that is the Sam Wanamaker Playhouse at Shakespeare's Globe on London's Bankside. This performance offers a chance to get up close with leading performers and Jonathan Cohen's crack Baroque ensemble, Arcangelo, which makes its Proms debut in works by Purcell, Blow, Locke and Draghi – including music for Shakespeare's *The Tempest*. See *'Poet, Playwright, Muse'*, pages 18–23.

RADIO *Live on BBC Radio 3 (3.00pm performance)*
ONLINE *Listen and catch up at bbc.co.uk/proms*

SPOTLIGHT ON...

Jonathan Cohen • Proms at ... Sam Wanamaker Playhouse

Shakespeare is the inspiration behind the two BBC Proms given by conductor Jonathan Cohen and his group Arcangelo, but by way of composers from half a century after the great Bard's time – Purcell, Blow, Locke and Draghi. 'The programme takes in *The Tempest* and *The Fairy Queen*, which is based on *A Midsummer Night's Dream*,' explains Cohen. 'Both Shakespeare plays were major inspirations for Purcell and others composers of the time, who wrote semi-operas or incidental music to complement them.' And, he continues, those scores could often be quite – well, unusual. 'I love the fantastical element to this music. Not bound to a plot or scene, the composer and librettist often went quite wild, frequently at a tangent to the play. The spectacle of fantastic and exotic acts as a kind of commentary on a scene was quite typical of the period.'

For Cohen, the Sam Wanamaker Playhouse is an ideal location for these events. 'In the intimacy of this wonderful small theatre, the audience will feel almost as if they are on stage, amid the performers. I love this bare, naked element.' And that, he feels, fits in perfectly with his broader aims for his respected period-instrument ensemble. 'In our work at Arcangelo, I like to encourage a real chamber music on stage, with a direct engagement with the music from each and every performer. The energy that brings suits an intimate venue like this, and also the music of the period.'

SATURDAY 13 AUGUST
PROM 38
7.00pm–c9.20pm • Royal Albert Hall

PRICE BAND D *Seats £18 to £68 (plus booking fee*)*
WEEKEND PROMMING PASS *see page 155*

JOHN WILSON

GEORGE AND IRA GERSHWIN REDISCOVERED

John Wilson Orchestra
John Wilson *conductor*

There will be one interval

John Wilson and his orchestra return to pay tribute to George and Ira Gershwin, one of America's most celebrated song-writing duos, with favourites including 'Embraceable You', 'Love Walked In', 'Fascinatin' Rhythm' and the ballet music from the 1951 film *An American in Paris*. See *'Two-Part Harmony'*, pages 96–97.

RADIO *Live on BBC Radio 3; recorded for future broadcast on BBC Radio 2*
TV *Broadcast on BBC Two this evening*
ONLINE *Listen, watch and catch up at bbc.co.uk/proms*

PROMS EXTRA

11.00am–1.00pm • **Imperial College Union** Proms Family Orchestra & Chorus – join professional musicians to create your own music inspired by this evening's Prom. Suitable for all the family (ages 7-plus). See pages 66–71 for details

2.00pm–4.00pm • **Imperial College Union** Join Edward Price and members of the BBC Singers to explore some of the most famous songs by lyricist Ira Gershwin. See pages 66–71 for details

5.15pm–6.00pm • **Imperial College Union** Edward Seckerson introduces the music of tonight's Gershwin Prom. *Edited version broadcast on BBC Radio 3 during tonight's interval*

SUNDAY 14 AUGUST

PROM 39
7.30pm–c10.05pm • Royal Albert Hall

PRICE BAND Ⓐ *Seats £7.50 to £38 (plus booking fee*)*
WEEKEND PROMMING PASS *see page 155*

SAKARI ORAMO

Haydn Symphony No. 34 in D minor *18'*

Charlotte Bray Falling in the Fire *c22'*
BBC commission: world premiere

INTERVAL

Mahler
Symphony No. 5 in C sharp minor *70'*

Guy Johnston *cello*

BBC Symphony Orchestra
Sakari Oramo *conductor*

The latest in the series of Proms cello concertos
is a powerful new work from Charlotte Bray, an
expression of 'moral outrage' at the destruction
of the ancient city of Palmyra, Syria, last summer,
after which 'everything changed' in the composer's
compositional outlook. Similarly, something changed
in Mahler when he came to write his Fifth
Symphony. Not only had he survived a
haemorrhage that had nearly killed him, but he
had also met and fallen in love with Alma Schindler,
for whom the Fifth Symphony's ardent Adagietto
is a love song. Before that, Haydn's Symphony
No. 34 makes its first appearance at the Proms.
See 'New Music', pages 86–95.

RADIO *Live on BBC Radio 3*
ONLINE *Listen and catch up at bbc.co.uk/proms*

PROMS EXTRA
5.45pm–6.30pm • Imperial College Union Composers in
Conversation: Charlotte Bray discusses her new work
Falling in the Fire and talks about her influences and
inspirations; with live performance and discussion.
Edited version broadcast on BBC Radio 3 after tonight's Prom

MONDAY 15 AUGUST

PROMS CHAMBER MUSIC 5
1.00pm–c2.00pm • Cadogan Hall

Seats £12/£14 (plus booking fee*)

STILE ANTICO

Morley It was a lover and his lass *4'*

Byrd O Lord, make thy servant Elizabeth;
Why do I use my paper, ink and pen? *6'*

Huw Watkins
The Phoenix and the Turtle *6'*

Byrd Fantasia a 5, 'Two parts in one
in the fourth above' *6'*

Tomkins Be strong and of a
good courage *3'*

Ramsey Sleep, fleshly birth *6'*

Byrd Browning a 5, 'The leaves be green' *4'*

Johnson Full fathom five *2'*

Nico Muhly Gentle sleep *7'*

Gibbons In nomine No. 1 *4'*

Wilbye Draw on, sweet night *6'*

Fretwork
Stile Antico

There will be no interval

Vocal ensemble Stile Antico and viol consort
Fretwork celebrate the Shakespeare anniversary,
contrasting music of his contemporaries with new
settings. See 'Poet, Playwright, Muse', pages 18–23.

RADIO *Live on BBC Radio 3*
ONLINE *Listen and catch up at bbc.co.uk/proms*

MONDAY 15 AUGUST

PROM 40
7.30pm–c9.30pm • Royal Albert Hall

PRICE BAND Ⓐ *Seats £7.50 to £38 (plus booking fee*)*

STEVEN ISSERLIS

Prokofiev
Symphony No. 1 in D major, 'Classical' *15'*

Francisco Coll
Four Iberian Miniatures *12'*
London premiere

INTERVAL

Thomas Adès Lieux retrouvés *15'*
world premiere of version with orchestra

Beethoven
Symphony No. 8 in F major *26'*

Augustin Hadelich *violin*
Steven Isserlis *cello*
Britten Sinfonia
Thomas Adès *conductor*

Thomas Adès's *Lieux retrouvés* was inspired by the
cello's 'haunting sense of time and place'. Here, Steven
Isserlis performs it in its new cello-and-orchestra
guise. Francisco Coll's piquant Iberian miniatures
contrast with 'Classical' symphonies by Prokofiev
and Beethoven. See 'New Music', pages 86–95.

RADIO *Live on BBC Radio 3*
ONLINE *Listen and catch up at bbc.co.uk/proms*

PROMS EXTRA
5.30pm–6.30pm • Radio Theatre, New Broadcasting House,
London The Aurora Orchestra performs the winning
pieces of the 2016 BBC Proms Inspire Young Composers'
Competition. *Tickets available from BBC Studio Audiences:
bbc.co.uk/showsandtours/shows.*

5.45pm–6.30pm • Imperial College Union Musicologist
John Deathridge discusses Beethoven's Symphony No. 8.
Edited version broadcast on BBC Radio 3 during tonight's interval

Sarah Lucas/Tony Clark (Oramo); Marco Borggreve (Stile Antico); Jean-Baptiste Millot (Isserlis)

TUESDAY 16 AUGUST

PROM 41
7.00pm–c9.15pm • Royal Albert Hall

PRICE BAND A *Seats £7.50 to £38 (plus booking fee*)*

ALICE COOTE

Berlioz Overture 'King Lear'   16'

Colin Matthews
Berceuse for Dresden   15'
London premiere

INTERVAL

Mahler Das Lied von der Erde   64'

Leonard Elschenbroich *cello*
Alice Coote *mezzo-soprano*
Gregory Kunde *tenor*

Hallé
Sir Mark Elder *conductor*

Berlioz's *King Lear* overture was admired by the King of Hanover: 'How you have portrayed [Cordelia] – her humility and tenderness! It is heart-rending, and so beautiful!' Continuing our focus on the cello this summer, Colin Matthews's *Berceuse for Dresden* takes inspiration from the eight bells of the Dresden church at which it was premiered. In Mahler's exploration of darkness and radiance in his culminating synthesis of song and symphony, *Das Lied von der Erde*, he altered the parameters of vocal and orchestral expression for ever. See 'New Music', pages 86–95.

RADIO *Live on BBC Radio 3*
TV *Recorded for broadcast on BBC Four on 25 August*
ONLINE *Listen, watch and catch up at bbc.co.uk/proms*

PROMS EXTRA

5.15pm–6.00pm • Imperial College Union Composers in Conversation: Colin Matthews, 70 this year, discusses his *Berceuse for Dresden* and talks about his influences and inspirations; with live performance and discussion.
Edited version broadcast on BBC Radio 3 during tonight's interval

TUESDAY 16 AUGUST

PROM 42
10.15pm–c11.30pm • Royal Albert Hall

PRICE BAND E *Seats £7.50 to £25 (plus booking fee*)*

HARRY CHRISTOPHERS

J. S. Bach
Komm, Jesu, komm!, BWV 229   9'

Arvo Pärt Nunc dimittis   7'

J. S. Bach
Singet dem Herrn, BWV 225   14'

Arvo Pärt Triodion   14'

J. S. Bach
Jesu, meine Freude, BWV 227   20'

The Sixteen
Harry Christophers *conductor*

In this Late Night Prom Harry Christophers and his vocal group The Sixteen present a selection of J. S. Bach's rigorous yet deeply spiritual motets written in Leipzig in the 1720s, placing them against the resounding purity of sacred choral works by contemporary Estonian composer Arvo Pärt, including his *Nunc dimittis*, a cautious but luminous vision of eternity. An enlightening juxtaposition from one of the world's leading ensembles.

RADIO *Live on BBC Radio 3*
ONLINE *Listen and catch up at bbc.co.uk/proms*

WEDNESDAY 17 AUGUST

PROM 43
7.30pm–c9.40pm • Royal Albert Hall

PRICE BAND D *Seats £18 to £68 (plus booking fee*)*

MARTHA ARGERICH

Jörg Widmann Con brio   11'

Liszt
Piano Concerto No. 1 in E flat major   18'

INTERVAL

Wagner
Tannhäuser – overture   14'

Götterdämmerung – Dawn, Siegfried's
Rhine Journey and Funeral March   20'

The Mastersingers of Nuremberg
– overture   10'

Martha Argerich *piano*

West–Eastern Divan Orchestra
Daniel Barenboim *conductor*

Daniel Barenboim returns with his orchestra of young Arabs and Israelis, and with another iconic musician, Martha Argerich. Composer Jörg Widmann harnessed the energy of Beethoven's fast movements in the 'exercise in fury and rhythmic insistence' that is his *Con brio*. After Liszt's thunderously virtuosic First Piano Concerto, Daniel Barenboim – who conducted Wagner's *Ring* cycle at the Proms in 2013 – concludes with powerful excerpts from three of the composer's operas.

RADIO *Live on BBC Radio 3*
TV *Recorded for broadcast on BBC Four on 28 August*
ONLINE *Listen, watch and catch up at bbc.co.uk/proms*

PROMS EXTRA

5.45pm–6.30pm • Imperial College Union Musicologist Barbara Eichner explores Wagner's writing for the orchestra.
Edited version broadcast on BBC Radio 3 during tonight's interval

THURSDAY 18 AUGUST

PROM 44

7.30pm–c10.00pm • Royal Albert Hall

PRICE BAND **B** *Seats £9.50 to £48 (plus booking fee*)*

SHAKESPEARE: STAGE AND SCREEN

Walton, arr. M. Mathieson
Richard III – Prelude   8'

Finzi Love's Labour's Lost – suite   16'

Sullivan
The Tempest – Overture to Act 4   5'

Walton As You Like It – a poem for
orchestra after Shakespeare   6'

Joby Talbot The Winter's Tale
– Springtime Dance   6'

INTERVAL

Bernstein West Side Story –
Symphonic Dances   24'

Porter Kiss Me, Kate – excerpts   19'

Rodgers The Boys from Syracuse
– excerpts   17'

BBC Concert Orchestra
Keith Lockhart *conductor*

This transatlantic Prom presents a range of
Shakespeare's characters as reflected on stage and
screen – with an all-British first half and a second
half devoted to American musicals, conducted by
the US-born Keith Lockhart. See 'Poet, Playwright,
Muse', pages 18–23.

RADIO *Live on BBC Radio 3*
ONLINE *Listen and catch up at bbc.co.uk/proms*

PROMS EXTRA

5.45pm–6.30pm • Imperial College Union What is it like
to perform Shakespeare? And how does the playwright
portray the profession he knew best? A leading actor
discusses Shakespeare on stage.
Edited version broadcast on BBC Radio 3 during tonight's interval

c10.00pm–c11.00pm • Elgar Room, Royal Albert Hall
Georgia Mann-Smith presents informal late-night music and
poetry, featuring young talent. For details see bbc.co.uk/proms

FRIDAY 19 AUGUST

PROM 45

7.30pm–c9.55pm • Royal Albert Hall

PRICE BAND **B** *Seats £9.50 to £48 (plus booking fee*)*
WEEKEND PROMMING PASS *see page 155*

KARITA MATTILA

Janáček The Makropulos Affair   104'
(concert performance; sung in Czech)

Karita Mattila *Emilia Marty*
Aleš Briscein *Albert Gregor*
Gustáv Beláček *Dr Kolenatý*
Jan Vacík *Vítek*
Eva Štěrbová *Kristina*
Svatopluk Sem *Baron Jaroslav Prus*
Aleš Voráček *Janek*
Jan Ježek *Hauk-Šendorf*
Jiří Klecker *Stage Technician*
Yvona Škvárová *Cleaning Woman*
Jana Hrochová Wallingerová *Chambermaid*

BBC Singers (men's voices)
BBC Symphony Orchestra
Jiří Bělohlávek *conductor*

There will be one interval

A dream team gathers for Janáček's late, great
existential masterpiece *The Makropulos Affair*. This
tragic satire is powered by a score that contains
some of the composer's most extreme and alluring
music. The Finnish soprano acclaimed for her
'electrifying' portrayal of the opera's heroine, Emilia
Marty, at the Met in New York, is joined by Czech
musicians including the BBC Symphony Orchestra's
Conductor Laureate Jiří Bělohlávek.

RADIO *Live on BBC Radio 3*
ONLINE *Listen and catch up at bbc.co.uk/proms*

PROMS EXTRA

5.45pm–6.30pm • Imperial College Union Nigel Simeone
introduces Janáček's opera The Makropulos Affair.
Edited version broadcast on BBC Radio 3 during tonight's interval

SPOTLIGHT ON...

Jiří Bělohlávek • Prom 45

Czech conductor Jiří Bělohlávek is far from a
stranger to the BBC Proms, of course – as Chief
Conductor of the BBC Symphony Orchestra from
2006 to 2012, he's conducted dozens of Proms
events, including three Last Nights. 'Nobody will
be surprised that my strongest impression from the
wonderful BBC Proms festival was (and still is) the
incredible atmosphere of the Last Night,' he says,
'especially in 2012 – my farewell concert as Chief
Conductor with the BBC SO, which remains a
sacred moment in my memory.'

But it's one of his Czech homeland's most
mysterious operatic offerings that he conducts this
year, in a concert performance of Janáček's
thriller-cum-love-story *The Makropulos Affair*.
'I heard the opera for the first time on the
recording by František Jílek, and I remember the
fascination it left in my mind. It was a completely
new world of drama.'

Bělohlávek has conducted productions of
Makropulos in San Francisco and at The Met,
New York, both of them with Finnish soprano
Karita Mattila as the enigmatic central figure
of Emilia Marty. Mattila also sings the role at
this Prom, amid an otherwise all-Czech cast. 'She
proved to be the key to the musical and theatrical
approach to the work. She is the ideal artist for
this emotion-laden figure, and collaborating with
her has been among the strongest impressions
I have had during my opera career.'

SATURDAY 20 AUGUST

PROMS AT ... ROUNDHOUSE, CAMDEN *(see page 161)* 3.00pm–c4.30pm

Tickets £6 (plus booking fee*); for booking details, see pages 150–163

ANDREW GOURLAY

Programme to include:

Sir Harrison Birtwistle
The Message — 3'

Ligeti Ramifications — 9'

Georg Friedrich Haas
Open Spaces II — 16'
UK premiere

David Sawer April \ March — c20'
BBC co-commission: world premiere

London Sinfonietta
Andrew Gourlay *conductor*

There will be no interval

The Proms returns to Camden's industrial answer to the Royal Albert Hall for a programme which takes its lead from Ligeti's iconic *Ramifications*. This embracing score, for two groups of spatially positioned strings, is heard alongside music by one of Ligeti's natural musical heirs, Georg Friedrich Haas, and other new pieces concerned with physical space. The concert culminates in a major work from David Sawer that reflects the energy and physicality of dance. *See 'New Music', pages 86–95.*

RADIO *Live on BBC Radio 3*
ONLINE *Listen and catch up at bbc.co.uk/proms*

SATURDAY 20 AUGUST

PROM 46
7.30pm–c9.35pm • Royal Albert Hall

PRICE BAND Ⓐ *Seats £7.50 to £38 (plus booking fee*)*
WEEKEND PROMMING PASS *see page 155*

CAROLYN SAMPSON

Grisey Dérives — 13'
UK premiere

Mahler Rückert-Lieder — 20'

INTERVAL

Mozart Mass in C minor, K427 — 55'

Louise Alder *soprano*
Carolyn Sampson *soprano*
Tanja Ariane Baumgartner *mezzo-soprano*
Benjamin Hulett *tenor*
Matthew Rose *bass*

BBC Symphony Chorus
BBC Scottish Symphony Orchestra
Ilan Volkov *conductor*

Tonight's first half contrasts Gérard Grisey's classic *Dérives*, a striking exploration of the interiors of sounds, with Mahler's tender *Rückert-Lieder*. Mozart's unfinished Mass in C minor is a mix of the chamber and the operatic, the dancing and the devotional – a work ripe for the resonance of the Royal Albert Hall. *See 'New Music', pages 86–95.*

RADIO *Live on BBC Radio 3*
ONLINE *Listen and catch up at bbc.co.uk/proms*

PROMS EXTRA

1.00pm–4.00pm • Imperial College Union
Join Mary King and the BBC Singers to sing excerpts from Mozart's Mass in C minor. Experience in sight-reading or a knowledge of the piece is an advantage but not essential. *Suitable for ages 16-plus. See pages 66–71 for details*

5.45pm–6.30pm • Imperial College Union Timothy Jones introduces Mozart's Mass in C minor.
Edited version broadcast on BBC Radio 3 during tonight's interval

SPOTLIGHT ON...

Louise Alder • Prom 46

Mozart's Mass in C minor is a piece that British soprano Louise Alder has grown up with. 'My mother is a violinist in the Orchestra of the Age of Enlightenment and I've heard that orchestra play it over the years and been completely transported by it.' She's also been singing the Mass's sublime but vocally demanding 'Et incarnatus est' since she was a student: 'I vividly remember singing it in a 10.00am oratorio class and being commended for my bravery in doing it at that time in the morning.'

Alder – who made her Proms debut in 2014 taking over the role of Sophie in *Der Rosenkavalier* at short notice – has a busy schedule as a member of Frankfurt Opera, together with guest work for the Royal Opera, Glyndebourne and Garsington. This doesn't leave much time for appearing on the concert stage. 'It's a shame, because I absolutely love doing recitals and oratorios. However, Frankfurt has been good at letting me out to do as many other things as it can spare me for.'

As someone who adores singing Mozart, Alder hopes his operas will be a staple of her repertoire for years to come, and she finds his sacred masterpieces just as fulfilling. 'An aria such as "Et incarnatus est" is more lyrical and stretches the vocal limits more than the soubrette roles – such as Zerlina and Susanna – that I'm singing now in Mozart operas. So it's wonderful to be pushed and have that extra challenge.'

SUNDAY 21 AUGUST

PROM 47
3.45pm–c6.10pm • Royal Albert Hall

PRICE BAND Ⓐ *Seats £7.50 to £38 (plus booking fee*)*
WEEKEND PROMMING PASS *see page 155*

NAREK HAKHNAZARYAN

Piers Hellawell
Wild Flow   c20'
BBC commission: world premiere

Haydn
Cello Concerto No. 1 in C major   24'

INTERVAL

Tchaikovsky
Symphony No. 5 in E minor   50'

Narek Hakhnazaryan *cello*

Ulster Orchestra
Rafael Payare *conductor*

In the late 1880s Tchaikovsky felt momentarily
freed from the catastrophes that were haunting
his private life and carving a tragic path through
his career. His Fifth Symphony, which was taking
shape on his desk, appears to ease the composer's
own suffering. Light floods its textures; hopeful
melodies invade its dark corners. Venezuelan
conductor Rafael Payare makes his Proms debut
with his Ulster Orchestra to perform this most
radiant of Tchaikovsky's symphonies, bringing
with him Haydn's delightfully perky C major Cello
Concerto and a brand-new work by Piers Hellawell.
See 'New Music', pages 86–95.

RADIO *Live on BBC Radio 3*
ONLINE *Listen and catch up at bbc.co.uk/proms*

PROMS EXTRA

2.00pm–2.45pm • Imperial College Union Join professional
musicians for a family-friendly introduction to this afternoon's
Prom. Bring your instrument and join in! *Suitable for all the
family (ages 7-plus). See pages 66–71 for details*

SPOTLIGHT ON...
Rafael Payare • Prom 47

When Rafael Payare first came to the Proms,
he made his mark as Principal Horn of the
Simón Bolívar Orchestra. 'It was a life-changing
experience,' he says. And now, a few years on, the
Venezuelan musician returns to the Royal Albert
Hall as a conductor, with the Ulster Orchestra, of
which he has been Chief Conductor since 2014.
'It's very exciting! This is my second year with
Ulster and already we know each other much
better and are pushing the boundaries further.
There's less talking and more communicating
with just one look.'

It's not just the Royal Albert Hall that brings back
memories. Tchaikovsky's Fifth Symphony has a
special meaning too. 'Obviously it's a fantastic
piece with wonderful melodies,' Payare explains,
'and the second movement has this wonderful
horn solo, which I played many times and
recorded with Gustavo Dudamel.' Payare and
the Ulster Orchestra have also explored the Fifth
in a recent series dedicated to Tchaikovsky and
Beethoven. 'It's not like the Fourth or Sixth,
with lots of struggle,' he says. 'Here it's a bit
more about joy, with an ending of fireworks and
Russian flair.' Haydn's Cello Concerto and a
commission by Piers Hellawell, whose *Inside
Story* was premiered at the Proms in 1999,
complete the programme. 'Piers has been giving
me bits of the new score from time to time,' says
Payare. 'It's a great advantage when the composer
is alive, as you can talk to him!'

SUNDAY 21 AUGUST

PROM 48
7.30pm–c9.45pm • Royal Albert Hall

PRICE BAND Ⓐ *Seats £7.50 to £38 (plus booking fee*)*
WEEKEND PROMMING PASS *see page 155*

ALISA WEILERSTEIN

Matthias Pintscher
Reflections on Narcissus   35'

INTERVAL

Mendelssohn
A Midsummer Night's Dream –
overture and incidental music   66'

Katherine Broderick *soprano*
Clara Mouriz *mezzo-soprano*
Alisa Weilerstein *cello*

BBC Scottish Symphony Orchestra
Matthias Pintscher *conductor*

Narcissus, the Thespian hunter who fell in love
with his own image, inspired Matthias Pintscher to
compose his own reflection on 'the interaction of
different groups and their mirror images', a work for
cello and orchestra. Pintscher conducts *Reflections
on Narcissus* here before a semi-staged performance
of Mendelssohn's incidental music to *A Midsummer
Night's Dream*. Mendelssohn's delicate, mercurial
and strident music is interspersed with excerpts
from Shakespeare's text to form a centrepiece of
this season's celebrations of Shakespeare's 400th
anniversary. See 'Poet, Playwright, Muse', pages 18–23.

RADIO *Live on BBC Radio 3*
ONLINE *Listen and catch up at bbc.co.uk/proms*

PROMS EXTRA
5.45pm–6.30pm • Imperial College Union The Herdwick
Shepherd, James Rebanks, talks about his profession as
depicted in Shakespeare's plays and how it has changed over
400 years. He is joined on stage by a Shakespeare expert.
Edited version broadcast on BBC Radio 3 during tonight's interval

Marco Borggreve (Hakhnazaryan); Luis Cabelo (Payare); Harald Hoffmann/Decca (Weilerstein)

20–21 AUGUST

MONDAY 22 AUGUST

PROMS CHAMBER MUSIC 6
1.00pm–c2.00pm • Cadogan Hall

Seats £12/£14 (plus booking fee)*

LOUIS LORTIE

Rossini, arr. Liszt
Soirées musicales – La regata veneziana
(notturno); La danza (tarantella)   5'

Fauré
Barcarolle No. 5 in F sharp minor, Op. 66   6'

Barcarolle No. 7 in D minor, Op. 90   6'

Poulenc Napoli   15'

Liszt Venezia e Napoli   20'

Louis Lortie *piano*

There will be no interval

Eloquent French-Canadian pianist Louis Lortie
performs an intriguing programme that moves
from the clear spring-water of Fauré's Barcarolles
to depictions of Italian cities from Poulenc and Liszt.
Poulenc's pianistic vision of Naples manages to be
light-hearted and dazzling at the same time. Liszt
was intrigued and inspired by the city's furious
traditional dance, the tarantella. He used that and
the gondola songs of Venice in the broad emotional
canvas that is his *Venezia e Napoli*.

RADIO *Live on BBC Radio 3*
ONLINE *Listen and catch up at bbc.co.uk/proms*

MONDAY 22 AUGUST

PROM 49
7.30pm–c9.45pm • Royal Albert Hall

PRICE BAND Ⓒ *Seats £14 to £58 (plus booking fee*)*

QUINCY JONES

QUINCY JONES PROM

Quincy Jones

Richard Bona *voice/bass guitar*
Jacob Collier *voice/piano/synth*
James Morrison *trumpet*
Alfredo Rodríguez *piano*

Metropole Orkest
Jules Buckley *conductor*

There will be one interval

Jules Buckley and his Metropole Orkest return to
the Proms to celebrate the career of composer,
arranger, conductor, producer and all-round musical
giant Quincy Jones. Recent musical partners of
Quincy's join the longest-established jazz orchestra
in existence as special guests to collaborate on new
arrangements of hits both old and new – and the
great man himself makes an appearance.

RADIO *Live on BBC Radio 3*
TV *Broadcast on BBC Four this evening*
ONLINE *Listen, watch and catch up at bbc.co.uk/proms*

PROMS EXTRA
5.45pm–6.30pm • Imperial College Union *Conductor*
Jules Buckley introduces the music of tonight's Prom.
Edited version broadcast on BBC Radio 3 during tonight's interval

SPOTLIGHT ON...

Jules Buckley • Prom 49

As a child of the 1980s, Jules Buckley first came
across Quincy Jones's work through the Michael
Jackson albums that Jones produced. 'We had
Thriller on in the car when I was aged 3,'
remembers the Metropole Orkest's British-born
Chief Conductor. 'In my teenage years, when
I started buying records, I began finding all kinds
of music that Quincy worked on, from pop to jazz
to films. And, as I became an arranger, I realised
he was the god of that field.'

So, how do you celebrate a musical giant whose
career has spanned so many genres, and so many
identities, from jazz trumpeter, conductor and
composer to producer, arranger and manager? 'My
aim,' says Buckley, 'is to showcase Quincy's best
work, not simply his most well-known material.
We'll be looking back at his big-band work and his
film scores, but also looking forwards, as Richard
Bona Jacob Collier, James Morrison and Alfredo
Rodríguez – four artists whom Quincy has been
supporting as mentor or manager – re-imagine
some of his better-known works.'

Buckley was in Los Angeles earlier this year,
doing what Jones has done many times before –
picking up a Grammy. The award, for *Sylva*,
the Metropole Orkest's album with American
jazz-fusion collective Snarky Puppy, was the
orchestra's third Grammy; Jones has 27.
'Yes, we've got a way to go before we catch
up with Quincy!' laughs Buckley.

TUESDAY 23 AUGUST

PROM 50
7.30pm–c9.35pm • Royal Albert Hall

PRICE BAND A *Seats £7.50 to £38 (plus booking fee*)*

STEPHEN HOUGH

Tchaikovsky
Fantasy-Overture 'Hamlet'   *18'*

Rachmaninov
Rhapsody on a Theme of Paganini   *23'*

INTERVAL

Prokofiev
Symphony No. 3 in C minor   *34'*

Stephen Hough *piano*

BBC Symphony Chorus
BBC Symphony Orchestra
Alexander Vedernikov *conductor*

In 1919 Prokofiev started work on his opera *The Fiery Angel*, a touching love story set against the backdrop of demonic possession. He recast much of the opera's most impactful music into his Third Symphony. Alexander Vedernikov conducts it here after Stephen Hough plays Rachmaninov's devilish and ever-entertaining 'Paganini' Variations, and the final instalment of fellow Russian Tchaikovsky's three Shakespeare overtures. See 'Poet, Playwright, Muse', pages 18–23.

RADIO *Live on BBC Radio 3*
ONLINE *Listen and catch up at bbc.co.uk/proms*

PROMS EXTRA
5.45pm–6.30pm • Imperial College Union Popular myth suggests that the violinist and composer Paganini sold his soul to the Devil in order to become a musical prodigy. Ahead of tonight's performance of Rachmaninov's *Rhapsody on a Theme of Paganini*, Rev. Richard Coles and poet Imtiaz Dharker discuss the Devil in Christian and Islamic cultures.
Edited version broadcast on BBC Radio 3 during tonight's interval

WEDNESDAY 24 AUGUST

PROM 51
7.00pm–c9.15pm • Royal Albert Hall

PRICE BAND B *Seats £9.50 to £48 (plus booking fee*)*

GABRIELA MONTERO

Marlos Nobre Kabbalah   *10'*
UK premiere

Grieg Piano Concerto in A minor   *30'*

INTERVAL

Villa-Lobos
Bachianas brasileiras No. 4 – Prelude   *8'*

Rachmaninov Symphonic Dances   *36'*

Gabriela Montero *piano*

São Paulo Symphony Orchestra
Marin Alsop *conductor*

This year's Proms focus on Latin America in the year the Olympic Games go to Rio de Janeiro heats up with a visit from the São Paulo Symphony Orchestra under its charismatic conductor Marin Alsop. Their concert is bookended by infectious, furious dances from Marlos Nobre and Rachmaninov. In between comes music from the doyen of South American composers, Heitor Villa-Lobos, and a performance of Grieg's Piano Concerto for which the orchestra is joined by Venezuelan pianist Gabriela Montero. See 'Latin Leaders', pages 98–99.

RADIO *Live on BBC Radio 3*
TV *Broadcast on BBC Four this evening*
ONLINE *Listen, watch and catch up at bbc.co.uk/proms*

PROMS EXTRA
5.15pm–6.00pm • Imperial College Union
Arthur Nestrovski, Artistic Director of the São Paulo Symphony Orchestra, discusses the life and work of the orchestra.
Edited version broadcast on BBC Radio 3 during tonight's interval

WEDNESDAY 24 AUGUST

PROM 52
10.15pm–c11.30pm • Royal Albert Hall

PRICE BAND E *Seats £7.50 to £25 (plus booking fee*)*

MARIN ALSOP

Strings of the São Paulo Symphony Orchestra
São Paulo Jazz Symphony Orchestra
Marin Alsop *conductor*

Immediately following the São Paulo Symphony Orchestra's evening Prom, its string players and Principal Conductor Marin Alsop are joined by members of the São Paulo Jazz Symphony Orchestra for a landmark celebration of Brazilian popular-music from the past 100 years. Few countries can boast such an ingrained and individual popular music tradition as Brazil, and this feel-good Late Night Prom will take you from the African-influenced rhythms and Chopinesque chromaticism of Brazilian street music to the outlandish constructions of the so-called São Paulo avant-garde – all from the best Brazilian players in the business.

RADIO *Live on BBC Radio 3; recorded for future broadcast on BBC Radio 6 Music*
TV/iPLAYER *Watch from tomorrow at bbc.co.uk/proms*
ONLINE *Listen, watch and catch up at bbc.co.uk/proms*

THURSDAY 25 AUGUST

PROM 53
7.30pm–c9.40pm • Royal Albert Hall

PRICE BAND Ⓐ *Seats £7.50 to £38 (plus booking fee*)*

VASILY PETRENKO

Emily Howard Torus   c20'
BBC commission: world premiere

Shostakovich
Cello Concerto No. 1 in E flat major   29'

INTERVAL

Rachmaninov
Symphony No. 3 in A minor   40'

Truls Mørk *cello*

Royal Liverpool Philharmonic Orchestra
Vasily Petrenko *conductor*

'A composer's music should express his love affairs, his religion, the books that have influenced him, the pictures he loves.' So said Rachmaninov, whose Third Symphony does just that through irrepressible yearning and longing. It forms the culmination of this Prom in which the Royal Liverpool Philharmonic Orchestra and its Russian Chief Conductor perform Shostakovich's disquieting First Cello Concerto. A brand-new work by Liverpool-born composer Emily Howard opens. See 'New Music', pages 86–95.

RADIO *Live on BBC Radio 3*
ONLINE *Listen and catch up at bbc.co.uk/proms*

PROMS EXTRA
5.45pm–6.30pm • Imperial College Union Composers in Conversation: Emily Howard discusses the world premiere of her new work Torus and talks about her influences and inspirations; with live performances and discussion. *Edited version broadcast on BBC Radio 3 after tonight's Prom*

c9.50pm–c10.50pm • Elgar Room, Royal Albert Hall
Georgia Mann-Smith presents informal late-night music and poetry, featuring young talent. *For details see bbc.co.uk/proms*

FRIDAY 26 AUGUST

PROM 54
7.30pm–c9.45pm • Royal Albert Hall

PRICE BAND Ⓒ *Seats £14 to £58 (plus booking fee*)*
WEEKEND PROMMING PASS *see page 155*

JEREMY OVENDEN

Mozart
Aria, 'Per questa bella mano', K612   8'
Clarinet Concerto in A major, K622   28'

INTERVAL

Requiem (compl. Süssmayr)   55'

Ákos Ács *clarinet*
Lucy Crowe *soprano*
Barbara Kozelj *mezzo-soprano*
Jeremy Ovenden *tenor*
Neal Davies *bass*

Collegium Vocale Gent
Budapest Festival Orchestra
Iván Fischer *conductor*

The story of Mozart's last months is almost as remarkable as the string of masterpieces he produced during them. Who was the cloaked figure rumoured to have commissioned Mozart to write the Requiem? We'll never know, but the deathly tread, furious fight and radiant hope of the music remain unparalleled. Iván Fischer brings his equally exceptional Budapest Festival Orchestra to the Proms, joined by one of Europe's leading choirs for the Requiem, alongside the autumnal shades of Mozart's late Clarinet Concerto.

RADIO *Live on BBC Radio 3*
TV *Broadcast on BBC Four this evening*
ONLINE *Listen, watch and catch up at bbc.co.uk/proms*

PROMS EXTRA
5.45pm–6.30pm • Imperial College Union Sir Nicholas Kenyon introduces Mozart's Requiem and the mythology around the music. *Edited version broadcast on BBC Radio 3 during tonight's interval*

SATURDAY 27 AUGUST

PROM 55
7.30pm–c9.35pm • Royal Albert Hall

PRICE BAND Ⓐ *Seats £7.50 to £38 (plus booking fee*)*
WEEKEND PROMMING PASS *see page 155*

BARBARA HANNIGAN

Mozart
The Magic Flute – overture   7'

Hans Abrahamsen
let me tell you   35'
London premiere

INTERVAL

Tchaikovsky
Symphony No. 4 in F minor   44'

Barbara Hannigan *soprano*

City of Birmingham Symphony Orchestra
Mirga Gražinytė-Tyla *conductor*

The City of Birmingham Symphony Orchestra makes its first London appearance with young Lithuanian Mirga Gražinytė-Tyla, who becomes the orchestra's Music Director next season. While Mozart's overture combines infectious energy with Masonic symbolism, Tchaikovsky's dramatic Fourth Symphony explores the shadow cast by Fate. Hans Abrahamsen's Grawemeyer Award-winning song-cycle for Barbara Hannigan centres on Shakespeare's Ophelia, using only words allotted to her in Hamlet. See 'New Music', pages 86–95.

RADIO *Live on BBC Radio 3*
TV *Recorded for broadcast on BBC Four on 4 September*
ONLINE *Listen, watch and catch up at bbc.co.uk/proms*

PROMS EXTRA
5.45pm–6.30pm • Imperial College Union Writer Rosamund Bartlett discusses Tchaikovsky's Symphony No. 4. *Edited version broadcast on BBC Radio 3 during tonight's interval*

SPOTLIGHT ON...

Mirga Gražinytė-Tyla • Prom 55

Mirga Gražinytė-Tyla made the headlines when she was recently announced as the next Music Director of the City of Birmingham Symphony Orchestra, following in the footsteps of Sir Simon Rattle, among others. This Prom will be their first London outing together since the appointment. 'It's very exciting and inspiring that this is our opening gesture,' she says. 'I'm dreaming a lot about what will be possible with this incredible orchestra.'

Tchaikovsky's Fourth Symphony was a natural choice for this new team's Prom. 'For our very first music-making together last year we performed selections from his *Sleeping Beauty* ballet, so to come back to Tchaikovsky will be great,' explains Gražinytė-Tyla. 'He was always very important to me. I remember the first time I was occupied by his symphonies, I was reading Dostoyevsky and there is a very close relationship between this music and literature.'

Shakespeare meanwhile, is the inspiration behind Hans Abrahamsen's *let me tell you*, a song-cycle written for soprano Barbara Hannigan. 'It has incredibly strong poetry on both literary and musical levels, and a simplicity and quietness,' says Gražinytė-Tyla. 'I'm also so glad we will be working with Barbara. I don't know her personally yet, but we are both involved with a German film that's being made featuring four female conductors. Barbara both sings and conducts. To perform together will be a great gift.'

SUNDAY 28 AUGUST

PROM 56
11.00am–c12.00pm • Royal Albert Hall

PRICE BAND (H) *Seats £7.50 to £20 (plus booking fee*)*

GEMMA HUNT

CBEEBIES PROM

Presenters to include:

Andy Day *(from 'Andy's Dinosaur Adventures')*
Ben Faulks *(Mr Bloom)*
Gemma Hunt *(from 'Swashbuckle')*
Chris Jarvis *(from 'Show Me, Show Me' and 'Stargazing')*
Rebecca Keatley *(from 'Let's Play')*
Steven Kynman *(Robert the Robot)*
Cat Sandion *(CBeebies presenter)*

BBC Concert Orchestra
Jessica Cottis *conductor*

There will be no interval

Join the BBC Concert Orchestra and some of CBeebies' best-loved presenters and characters in a special musical journey. Aimed at 0- to 5-year-olds and their families, this Prom takes the audience on a journey through time and space, from dinosaur adventures with Andy to swashbuckling treasure-hunts with Gemma and stargazing with Chris. The magical world of CBeebies is brought to life by orchestral classics. *See 'Family Values', pages 68–71.*

Sign-interpreted performance: see page 162 for details

TV *Recorded for future broadcast on CBeebies*
ONLINE *Watch and catch up at bbc.co.uk/proms*

PROMS EXTRA
12.30pm–2.30pm • Imperial College Union Continue your CBeebies family adventure at the Proms and join in our range of activities from arts and crafts to music and dance. You never know, your favourite CBeebies character might even pop in to say hello! *Suitable for all ages. For sign-up information, see page 69*

SUNDAY 28 AUGUST

PROM 57
7.30pm–c9.50pm • Royal Albert Hall

PRICE BAND (A) *Seats £7.50 to £38 (plus booking fee*)*
WEEKEND PROMMING PASS *see page 155*

ELIZABETH KULMAN

Thomas Larcher
Symphony No. 2   35'
UK premiere

Wagner Wesendonck-Lieder   21'

INTERVAL

Strauss An Alpine Symphony   49'

Elisabeth Kulman *mezzo-soprano*

BBC Symphony Orchestra
Semyon Bychkov *conductor*

An Alpine Symphony combines the tunefulness, richness of orchestration and sheer unadulterated beauty of Richard Strauss's character-based tone-poems with what is probably his most impressive piece of musical architecture. Whether depicting a bracing mountain climb or the slow formation of the mountain range itself, the work has a magnificence all of its own, particularly when resounding through the Royal Albert Hall. The BBC Symphony Orchestra under Semyon Bychkov scales its heights here, after Wagner's unalloyed love songs for Mathilde Wesendonck and the first UK performance of Thomas Larcher's Symphony No. 2. *See 'New Music', pages 86–95.*

RADIO *Live on BBC Radio 3*
ONLINE *Listen and catch up at bbc.co.uk/proms*

PROMS EXTRA
5.45pm–6.30pm • Imperial College Union Strauss expert William Mival introduces the epic *An Alpine Symphony*. *Edited version broadcast on BBC Radio 3 during tonight's interval*

MONDAY 29 AUGUST

PROM 58
11.00am–c12.00pm • Royal Albert Hall

PRICE BAND (H) *Seats £7.50 to £20 (plus booking fee*)*

ROBERT THE ROBOT

CBEEBIES PROM

Presenters to include:

Andy Day *(from 'Andy's Dinosaur Adventures')*
Ben Faulks *(Mr Bloom)*
Gemma Hunt *(from 'Swashbuckle')*
Chris Jarvis *(from 'Show Me, Show Me'
and 'Stargazing')*
Rebecca Keatley *(from 'Let's Play')*
Steven Kynman *(Robert the Robot)*
Cat Sandion *(CBeebies presenter)*

BBC Concert Orchestra
Jessica Cottis *conductor*

There will be no interval

See 'Family Values', pages 68–71.

For concert description, see Prom 56

RADIO *Live on BBC Radio 3*
ONLINE *Listen and catch up at bbc.co.uk/proms*

PROMS EXTRA
12.30pm–2.30pm • Imperial College Union Continue your
CBeebies family adventure at the Proms and join in our
range of activities from arts and crafts to music and dance.
You never know, your favourite CBeebies character might
even pop in to say hello! *Suitable for all ages. For sign-up
information, see page 69*

MONDAY 29 AUGUST

PROMS CHAMBER MUSIC 7
1.00pm–c2.00pm • Cadogan Hall

Seats £12/£14 (plus booking fee*)

ARMIDA QUARTET

Schubert
Quartettsatz in C minor, D703   9'

Sally Beamish Merula perpetua   c10'
BBC co-commission: world premiere

Mozart
String Quintet in C major, K515   36'

Armida Quartet
Lise Berthaud *viola*
David Saudubray *piano*

There will be no interval

BBC Radio 3 New Generation Artists the Armida
Quartet bring two friends and three composers
to Cadogan Hall for the summer's seventh Proms
Chamber Music concert. Either side of a new work
for viola and piano written for Lise Berthaud and
David Saudubray by Sally Beamish are chamber
works by Schubert and Mozart: the former's
quartet movement combining sobriety and vivacity,
and the latter's C major String Quintet – a work
brimming with twists, interruptions and thrills.
See 'New Music', pages 86–95.

RADIO *Live on BBC Radio 3*
ONLINE *Listen and catch up at bbc.co.uk/proms*

MONDAY 29 AUGUST

PROM 59
7.30pm–c9.50pm • Royal Albert Hall

PRICE BAND (D) *Seats £18 to £68 (plus booking fee*)*
WEEKEND PROMMING PASS *see page 155*

SIR ANDRÁS SCHIFF

Beethoven
Overture 'Leonore' No. 2   14'
Piano Concerto No. 5 in E flat major,
'Emperor'   38'

INTERVAL

Symphony No. 7 in A major   38'

Sir András Schiff *piano*

Leipzig Gewandhaus Orchestra
Herbert Blomstedt *conductor*

Tonight's all-Beethoven Prom culminates in the
composer's most fascinating and bold symphony,
a piece shaped by irresistible rhythmic drive,
whether in the inevitable tread of its slow march
or the propulsive energy of its outer movements.
One of the world's oldest orchestras, along with
one of its closest collaborators, lights the fuse on
Beethoven's Seventh and his excitable *Leonore*
Overture No. 2, while 'pianist's pianist' Sir András
Schiff performs the composer's most commanding
piano concerto.

RADIO *Live on BBC Radio 3*
ONLINE *Listen and catch up at bbc.co.uk/proms*

PROMS EXTRA
5.45pm–6.30pm • Imperial College Union As the Leipzig
Gewandhaus Orchestra performs at the Proms, novelist
Philip Kerr and historian Karen Leeder talk about East
and West Germany, their differences and similarities and
how massive peaceful demonstrations in Leipzig in 1989
triggered the fall of the Berlin Wall.
Edited version broadcast on BBC Radio 3 during tonight's interval

CONCERT LISTINGS

SPOTLIGHT ON...
Herbert Blomstedt • Prom 59

'Beethoven is the towering master for symphonic music,' says Herbert Blomstedt, relishing the prospect of an all-Beethoven programme with his former band, the Leipzig Gewandhaus Orchestra. 'His music is the most challenging and demanding – every work charged with depth and meaning to the ultimate degree. When taken seriously, there is no more exciting music. Every performance is like climbing a mountain. And it gets bigger and bigger. The view is gorgeous.'

Blomstedt still recalls the time he took up the baton in Leipzig, in 1998, after a decade in San Francisco: 'In a way it was like coming home to the musical soil that had nurtured my love for music from the very beginning. The orchestra had been through tough times, but their traditions and their dedication carried them to new heights. Nowhere is music more dominant in a city than in Leipzig. Their musicians are the pride of the whole city.' They'll be joined for the 'Emperor' Concerto by Sir András Schiff, a pianist Blomstedt admires for his 'deep insight, revealing both the intellectual and emotional qualities of the music, and served with elegance and grace'.

Blomstedt's personal Proms record includes memorable concerts with the Gewandhaus in 2001 (his Proms debut) and with the Gustav Mahler Youth Orchestra, back in 2010: 'I love the Proms, the endless enthusiasm of its youthful public and its truly democratic outreach.'

Martin U. K. Lengemann (Blomstedt); Jim Rakete/Sony Classical (Gerhaher); J. Kravetz/mbv/ag/Getty Images (Washington)

TUESDAY 30 AUGUST

PROM 60
7.00pm–c9.05pm • Royal Albert Hall

PRICE BAND B Seats £9.50 to £48 (plus booking fee*)

CHRISTIAN GERHAHER

J. S. Bach
Cantata No. 82, 'Ich habe genug'   22'

INTERVAL

Bruckner
Symphony No. 9 in D minor   64'

Christian Gerhaher bass-baritone

Gustav Mahler Jugendorchester
Philippe Jordan conductor

Death laid its hand on Anton Bruckner as he laboured over the incomplete last movement of his final symphony. But as life was leaving Bruckner, vision and faith were only strengthening in him. Even in its incompleteness, Bruckner's Ninth carries with it an inspiring optimism in the face of death. 'Art had its beginning in God,' believed Bruckner, 'and so it must lead back to God.' Appropriate sentiments given it is preceded by Bach's cantata of resignation and acceptance 'Ich habe genug' from the thrilling bass-baritone of Christian Gerhaher.

RADIO Live on BBC Radio 3
ONLINE Listen and catch up at bbc.co.uk/proms

PROMS EXTRA
5.15pm–6.00pm • Imperial College Union Broadcaster and journalist Stephen Johnson introduces Bruckner's Ninth Symphony and discusses the life and work of the composer. Edited version broadcast on BBC Radio 3 during tonight's interval

TUESDAY 30 AUGUST

PROM 61
10.15pm–c11.30pm • Royal Albert Hall

PRICE BAND E £7.50 to £25 (plus booking fee*)

KAMASI WASHINGTON

Kamasi Washington saxophone

Strings of the City of Birmingham Symphony Orchestra
Jules Buckley conductor

There will be no interval

Thrilling California-based saxophonist and composer Kamasi Washington has been described as the biggest thing to hit jazz for years. Having toured for over a decade with artists such as Herbie Hancock, Lauryn Hill and Snoop Dogg, he now brings his own band to the Proms, combining with the strings of the City of Birmingham Symphony Orchestra, along with choral backing, to perform tracks from his groundbreaking recent three-disc album The Epic.

RADIO Live on BBC Radio 3
ONLINE Listen and catch up at bbc.co.uk/proms

WEDNESDAY 31 AUGUST

PROM 62
7.30pm–c9.45pm • Royal Albert Hall

PRICE BAND A *Seats £7.50 to £38 (plus booking fee*)*

BAIBA SKRIDE

Bayan Northcott
Concerto for Orchestra   c15'
BBC commission: world premiere

Mozart Violin Concerto
No. 5 in A major, K219 'Turkish'   29'

INTERVAL

Zemlinsky Lyric Symphony   46'

Baiba Skride *violin*
Siobhan Stagg *soprano*
Christopher Maltman *baritone*

BBC Symphony Orchestra
Simone Young *conductor*

Simone Young makes her Proms debut with the
world premiere of Bayan Northcott's *Concerto for
Orchestra* and Mozart's Eastern-influenced violin
concerto. Then, a rare chance to hear Zemlinsky's
setting of Hindu poetry by Rabindranath Tagore,
an alluring and mysterious slice of late-Romantic
lusciousness in which soprano and baritone drape
verses over a kaleidoscopic orchestra. See 'New
Music', pages 86–95.

RADIO *Live on BBC Radio 3*
ONLINE *Listen and catch up at bbc.co.uk/proms*

PROMS EXTRA
5.45pm–6.30pm • Imperial College Union Tonight's Prom
features a setting by Zemlinsky of 'The Gardener' by the great
Bengali poet and Nobel Laureate Rabindranath Tagore.
Novelist Tahmima Anam and BBC Radio 3 New Generation
Thinker Preti Taneja, from the University of Warwick/
Queen Mary University of London, discuss the poem
and Tagore's place in both Bengali and world culture.
Edited version broadcast on BBC Radio 3 during tonight's interval

THURSDAY 1 SEPTEMBER

PROM 63
7.30pm–c9.35pm • Royal Albert Hall

PRICE BAND C *Seats £14 to £58 (plus booking fee*)*

KATHERINE WATSON

J. S. Bach Mass in B minor   110'

Katherine Watson *soprano*
Tim Mead *counter-tenor*
Reinoud Van Mechelen *tenor*
André Morsch *baritone*

Les Arts Florissants
William Christie *conductor*

There will be no interval

During the last four years of his life, Johann
Sebastian Bach worked on a piece that he knew
would represent the summation of his life's work.
In the end, the material of Bach's almighty Mass in
B minor was almost two decades in the making – a
compilation of some of his finest vocal music woven
together with startlingly original new music born of
acute inspiration. William Christie conducts Bach's
Mass with a quartet of soloists and his own
ensemble Les Arts Florissants, known for its
historically informed and infectiously exciting
performances of Baroque music.

RADIO *Live on BBC Radio 3*
ONLINE *Listen and catch up at bbc.co.uk/proms*

PROMS EXTRA
5.45pm–6.30pm • Imperial College Union In celebration
of the cello at this summer's Proms, join us for a special
screening of Paul Tortelier's 1964 masterclass on Bach's Suite
No. 3 in C major for solo cello. In this rarely seen archive
footage the French cello virtuoso tutors two students
through performance and discussion.

c9.45pm–c10.45pm • Elgar Room, Royal Albert Hall
Georgia Mann-Smith presents informal late-night
music and poetry featuring emerging UK talent.
For details see bbc.co.uk/proms

SPOTLIGHT ON...

William Christie • Prom 63

'The Royal Albert Hall is the happiness hall!'
The distinguished US-born, French-resident
conductor William Christie is far from a stranger
to the Proms and performing here is clearly
something he cherishes. 'The audience is the
best in the world. There are thousands of them
and they peer down at you from all around.
They're there to enjoy the performance, obviously,
but they're immensely supportive as well.
And every time I've been there it's been with
something I've desperately wanted to present
to a London audience.'

This year is no exception. Christie is renowned
for his sparkling period interpretations, especially
of music from the French Baroque, and for having
brought composers such as Rameau and Lully
back into the public consciousness virtually
single-handedly. But it's a very different beast
he tackles this year: Bach's Mass in B minor.
'When you're in front of a piece like this, you
feel wonderfully fortunate,' he says. 'This will
be only the second time I've conducted it, but
it comes at a marvellous moment in my life.
I don't think I could have said this 25 years ago,
but I feel like I've digested and assimilated an
awful lot of comment and scholarship, and
now I think I have something to say about
this piece. And essentially it has to do with
me. Like everything I do, it will be an intensely
personal interpretation. But I believe in what
I'm doing.'

FRIDAY 2 SEPTEMBER

PROM 64
7.00pm–c8.55pm • Royal Albert Hall

PRICE BAND D *Seats £18 to £68 (plus booking fee*)*
WEEKEND PROMMING PASS *see page 155*

SIR SIMON RATTLE

Boulez Éclat   10'

Mahler Symphony No. 7   78'

Berlin Philharmonic
Sir Simon Rattle *conductor*

There will be no interval

Sir Simon Rattle brings his Berlin Philharmonic to the Proms for two concerts, the first falling on the day the festival commemorates the towering genius that was the late Pierre Boulez. Here Boulez's kaleidoscopic *Éclat* forms a prelude to perhaps Gustav Mahler's most radical symphony, a work in which his musical imagination stormed new territories in its fierce harmonies and wild scoring. In the symphony's celebrated 'Night Music' serenades – eerie yet strangely calming nocturnes for orchestra, one hinging on a gently strumming guitar and mandolin – Mahler appears to look to a realm far beyond his own.

RADIO *Live on BBC Radio 3*
TV *Broadcast on BBC Four this evening*
ONLINE *Listen, watch and catch up at bbc.co.uk/proms*

PROMS EXTRA
5.00pm–6.00pm • Imperial College Union *Counterpoint – The 2016 Final.* Paul Gambaccini chairs the Grand Final of the much-loved BBC Radio 4 music quiz, with amateur music-lovers from around the UK answering questions on a wide variety of music to decide who takes the trophy for 2016. This special recording marks the climax of *Counterpoint's* 30th-anniversary season. *Tickets available from BBC Studio Audiences, bbc.co.uk/showsandtours/shows. Edited version broadcast on BBC Radio 4 on 12 September*

FRIDAY 2 SEPTEMBER

PROM 65
10.15pm–c11.30pm • Royal Albert Hall

PRICE BAND F *Seats £10 to £35 (plus booking fee*)*
WEEKEND PROMMING PASS *see page 155*

ENSEMBLE INTERCONTEMPORAIN

Bartók Three Village Scenes   12'

Boulez Anthèmes 2   20'

Carter Penthode   20'

Boulez Cummings ist der Dichter   13'

BBC Singers
Ensemble Intercontemporain
Baldur Brönnimann *conductor*

There will be no interval

The Ensemble Intercontemporain commemorates the late Pierre Boulez – composer, conductor, polemicist and founder of the ensemble – with a programme of pieces he conducted during more than 40 years of appearances at the Proms. His *Anthèmes 2*, for violin and electronics, contrasts with the exuberant vocal setting of avian poetry by E. E. Cummings, performed by the BBC Singers. Around these come Bartók's earthy *Village Scenes* and Elliott Carter's *Penthode* – written for tonight's ensemble – a slow movement of geological power that has been compared to the steady glide of tectonic plates.

RADIO *Live on BBC Radio 3*
ONLINE *Listen and catch up at bbc.co.uk/proms*

SPOTLIGHT ON...

Baldur Brönnimann • Prom 65

'I think we're probably still too close to Boulez's death to say what his influences are, and what his achievements have been,' admits Swiss-born conductor Baldur Brönnimann, who conducts a Late Night Prom in tribute to the great Frenchman. 'He was a composer and conductor, and also an important figure within the music business and the political and cultural scene – his achievements are on many different levels.'

Brönnimann's concert intentionally ranges wider than simply music by Boulez, taking in Elliott Carter and Bartók too. 'It's the kind of programme that Boulez himself would have planned and this is what we're celebrating as well – his impact on the whole way music is programmed.' It's Brönnimann's debut as a performer at the Proms, although he's been in the audience many times before. 'I saw Boulez conducting several Proms – I lived in Manchester for a long time, so I would go down to London whenever I could. And of course the Proms has a great history of putting on great new music – I heard a lot of interesting new pieces for the first time there.'

He's conducting the eminent Ensemble Intercontemporain, the group Boulez founded in 1976. And he admits feeling a sense of responsibility to his late colleague. 'The ensemble is a living piece of performance history – the players know so many of the composers of today and they live and breathe this music.'

SATURDAY 3 SEPTEMBER
**PROMS AT ... BOLD TENDENCIES
MULTI-STOREY CAR PARK** (see page 160)
12.00pm–c1.00pm & 3.00pm–4.00pm

Tickets £6/£12 (plus booking fee*); for booking details,
see pages 150–163

CHRISTOPHER STARK

Steve Reich

Vermont Counterpoint	10'
Eight Lines	18'
Music for a Large Ensemble	18'

Multi-Story Orchestra
Christopher Stark conductor

There will be no interval

The Proms steps out of the Royal Albert Hall and
into a municipal car park in Peckham to salute the
man who reconnected art music to urban culture
in all its drive, repetition and asymmetry. South
London favourites Christopher Stark and the
Multi-Story Orchestra make their Proms debut
in an all-Reich performance on their home ground.
The programme includes Reich's bright and
excitable *Music for a Large Ensemble* – his first major
work for full orchestra – and the shifting patterns
of his single-movement 'octet' *Eight Lines*. See 'Music
for Spaces', pages 76–79.

RADIO Live on BBC Radio 3 (3.00pm performance)
ONLINE Listen and catch up at bbc.co.uk/proms

SATURDAY 3 SEPTEMBER
PROM 66
7.30pm–c9.35pm • Royal Albert Hall

PRICE BAND D Seats £18 to £68 (plus booking fee*)
WEEKEND PROMMING PASS see page 155

SIR SIMON RATTLE

Julian Anderson Incantesimi	5'
UK premiere	
Dvořák Slavonic Dances, Op. 46	36'

INTERVAL

| **Brahms** Symphony No. 2 in D major | 41' |

Berlin Philharmonic
Sir Simon Rattle conductor

Overlooking a lake in the Austrian resort of
Pörtschach, Johannes Brahms created a symphony
that captured all he saw: the beauty of the sunset;
the stillness of the night; the peaceful awakening to
a new day. And yet its musicians were to play, said
Brahms, as if 'with a mourning ribbon around their
arm'. Brahms's meeting of glowing melancholy and
piercing brightness is the culmination of the Berlin
Philharmonic's second Prom under Sir Simon Rattle,
following Dvořák's colourful *Slavonic Dances* and a
new work from Julian Anderson. See 'New Music',
pages 86–95.

RADIO Live on BBC Radio 3
ONLINE Listen and catch up at bbc.co.uk/proms

PROMS EXTRA
5.45pm–6.30pm • Imperial College Union Nicholas
Baragwanath introduces Brahms's Second Symphony.
Edited version broadcast on BBC Radio 3 during tonight's interval

SUNDAY 4 SEPTEMBER
PROM 67
3.45pm–c5.40pm • Royal Albert Hall

PRICE BAND C Seats £14 to £58 (plus booking fee*)
WEEKEND PROMMING PASS see page 155

GUSTAVO DUDAMEL

Paul Desenne Hipnosis mariposa	13'
UK premiere	
Villa-Lobos	
Bachianas brasileiras No. 2	22'

INTERVAL

Ravel	
Daphnis and Chloe – Suite No. 2	16'
La valse	12'

Simón Bolívar Symphony Orchestra
Gustavo Dudamel conductor

The incomparable Simón Bolívar Symphony
Orchestra makes a return following its second
appearance at the Proms back in 2011. As part
of our celebration this year of South American
music and musicians, we hear the performance
of Venezuelan composer Paul Desenne's *Hipnosis
mariposa* and Heitor Villa-Lobos's orchestral tribute
to J. S. Bach. This most thrusting of orchestras ends
with Ravel's dizzying parody of a *fin de siècle* waltz,
La valse. A Proms hot ticket if ever there was one.
See 'New Music', pages 86–95.

RADIO Live on BBC Radio 3
ONLINE Listen and catch up at bbc.co.uk/proms

PROMS EXTRA
2.00pm–2.45pm • Imperial College Union Join professional
musicians for a family-friendly introduction to this afternoon's
Prom. Bring your instrument and join in! *Suitable for all the
family (ages 7-plus). See pages 66–71 for details*

SUNDAY 4 SEPTEMBER

PROM 68
7.00pm–c10.50pm • Royal Albert Hall

PRICE BAND **B** *Seats £9.50 to £48 (plus booking fee*)*
WEEKEND PROMMING PASS *see page 155*

DANIELA BARCELLONA

Rossini Semiramide   *190'*
(concert performance; sung in Italian)

Albina Shagimuratova *Semiramide*
Daniela Barcellona *Arsace*
Ildebrando D'Arcangelo *Assur*
Javier Camarena *Idreno*
Gianluca Buratto *Oroe*
Susana Gaspar *Azema*
David Butt Philip *Mitrane*

Opera Rara Chorus
Orchestra of the Age of Enlightenment
Sir Mark Elder *conductor*

There will be one interval

Sir Mark Elder conducts Rossini's operatic tragedy, which pushes singers to the limits of expression in recounting the story of Semiramide, Queen of Babylon, and her entrapment in a web of incest and revenge at the behest of her long-lost son. Vocal athleticism, vivid storytelling and Classical poise combine in Rossini's rarely heard opera, performed in concert. See *'Theatre in the Blood'*, pages 24–27.

RADIO *Live on BBC Radio 3*
ONLINE *Listen and catch up at bbc.co.uk/proms*

PROMS EXTRA
12.30pm–3.30pm • Imperial College Union Join Mary King and members of the BBC Singers to sing excerpts from Rossini's *Semiramide*. Experience in sight-reading or a knowledge of the piece is an advantage but not essential. *Suitable for ages 16-plus*

5.15pm–6.00pm • Imperial College Union Musicologist Roger Parker introduces Rossini's final Italian opera. *Edited version broadcast on BBC Radio 3 during tonight's interval*

MONDAY 5 SEPTEMBER

PROMS CHAMBER MUSIC 8
1.00pm–c2.00pm • Cadogan Hall

Seats £12/£14 (plus booking fee*)

IESTYN DAVIES

Songs by Purcell (arr. Britten), Mendelssohn and Quilter, including settings of Shakespeare

Carolyn Sampson *soprano*
Iestyn Davies *counter-tenor*
Joseph Middleton *piano*

There will be no interval

Two cherished British singers round off 2016's Proms Chamber Music series with a joint recital at Cadogan Hall, celebrating English song with an extended stopover in Germany for songs and duets by Felix Mendelssohn. Either side, Carolyn Sampson, Iestyn Davies and Joseph Middleton present Benjamin Britten's touching 'realisations' of songs by the composer's theatrical predecessor Henry Purcell, and works by the doyen of English song, Roger Quilter. See *'Poet, Playwright, Muse'*, pages 18–23.

RADIO *Live on BBC Radio 3*
ONLINE *Listen and catch up at bbc.co.uk/proms*

MONDAY 5 SEPTEMBER

PROM 69
7.30pm–c9.55pm • Royal Albert Hall

PRICE BAND **C** *Seats £14 to £58 (plus booking fee*)*

DANIEL BARENBOIM

Mozart
Piano Concerto No. 24 in C minor, K491 *31'*

INTERVAL

Bruckner Symphony No. 4 in
E flat major, 'Romantic'   *69'*

Staatskapelle Berlin
Daniel Barenboim *piano/director*

Daniel Barenboim and his Staatskapelle Berlin open three consecutive evenings in which a Mozart piano concerto is paired with a Bruckner symphony. 'We shall never be able to do anything like that,' proclaimed Beethoven when he heard Mozart's dramatic, minor-key Piano Concerto No. 24. As with Mozart in his concertos, with each of Bruckner's symphonies came a keener focus of vision and honing of craft. With the Fourth, Bruckner really came of age, bringing a newfound confidence in the glowing first movement, while its statuesque Andante is a moving premonition of loss.

RADIO *Live on BBC Radio 3*
ONLINE *Listen and catch up at bbc.co.uk/proms*

PROMS EXTRA
5.45pm–6.30pm • Imperial College Union On the 300th anniversary of the birth of Lancelot 'Capability' Brown, historian Anna Pavord talks about his work and legacy. *Edited version broadcast on BBC Radio 3 during tonight's interval*

TUESDAY 6 SEPTEMBER

PROM 70
7.30pm–c9.45pm • Royal Albert Hall

PRICE BAND C *Seats £14 to £58 (plus booking fee*)*

DANIEL BARENBOIM

Mozart Piano Concerto No. 22
in E flat major, K482   *35'*

INTERVAL

Bruckner
Symphony No. 6 in A major   *53'*

Staatskapelle Berlin
Daniel Barenboim *piano/director*

Bruckner, but not as we know him. In the Sixth
Symphony, gone is the composer's typical heft, his
long-drawn crescendos and his archetypal brooding
introduction. Instead, this symphony gallops into life,
crackling with vitality. Bruckner's rich and individual
Sixth Symphony is heard in the second of the
Staatskapelle Berlin's two Proms after a piano
concerto by Mozart that boasts similar rarity and
individuality. Mozart's Piano Concerto No. 22 holds
a grace and majesty all of its own, 'unfolding like a
sovereign in progress', in the words of one
musicologist.

RADIO *Live on BBC Radio 3*
ONLINE *Listen and catch up at bbc.co.uk/proms*

PROMS EXTRA
5.45pm–6.30pm • Imperial College Union On this day 350
years ago the capital was in ruins after the Great Fire of
London. Historian Adrian Tinniswood describes the massive
clearing-up operation, with a new London emerging from
the old, and talks to New Generation Thinker Thomas
Charlton of Dr Williams's Library about the plans that
were drawn up for rebuilding the city.
Edited version broadcast on BBC Radio 3 during tonight's interval

WEDNESDAY 7 SEPTEMBER

PROM 71
7.30pm–c9.45pm • Royal Albert Hall

PRICE BAND C *Seats £14 to £58 (plus booking fee*)*

CHRISTIAN THIELEMANN

Mozart Piano Concerto No. 21
in C major, K467   *29'*

INTERVAL

Bruckner
Symphony No. 3 in D minor   *58'*

Daniil Trifonov *piano*

Staatskapelle Dresden
Christian Thielemann *conductor*

In the first of two Proms in which Christian
Thielemann displays his credentials as an interpreter
of the Austro-German repertoire, he focuses on
Bruckner's Third Symphony, the composer's
symphonic monument to his idol Wagner – a
monolithic memorial that feels at the same time
intimate and personal. Before that, one of the most
sought-after of today's pianists, Daniil Trifonov,
is the soloist in Mozart's Piano Concerto No. 21 –
whose ebullient finale contrasts with the seraphic
slow movement made famous by the 1967 film
Elvira Madigan.

RADIO *Live on BBC Radio 3*
ONLINE *Listen and catch up at bbc.co.uk/proms*

PROMS EXTRA
5.45pm–6.30pm • Imperial College Union Ahead of tonight's
concert, writer and broadcaster Gavin Plumley talks about
the life and work of the Staatskapelle Dresden and the
orchestra's place in German culture.
Edited version broadcast on BBC Radio 3 during tonight's interval

c10.00pm–c11.00pm • Elgar Room, Royal Albert Hall
Georgia Mann-Smith presents informal late-night
music and poetry featuring emerging UK talent.
For details see bbc.co.uk/proms

SPOTLIGHT ON...
Daniil Trifonov • Prom 71

'Meteoric' is a word that's probably used too often
to describe the upward trajectories of musicians'
careers. But, in the case of young Russian pianist
Daniil Trifonov, it seems pretty apt. It was only
five years ago that he won two of the piano world's
top contests – the Rubinstein and Tchaikovsky
competitions – within weeks of each other, and
he's now in demand around the world as one of
today's very finest players.

He made his Proms debut in 2013, playing
Glazunov's rarely heard Second Concerto, and
was one of the pianists who tackled Prokofiev's
complete piano concertos in a single Prom last
year. But it's a very different piece he brings to this
year's festival: Mozart's Piano Concerto No. 21.
'I learnt this concerto while I was a student at
the Moscow Gnessin School,' Trifonov explains,
'it was one of the pieces that made me, as a kid,
adore Mozart's music. It's a great joy to return to
it after many years of not playing it. Mozart is one
of the most difficult composers for a pianist –
every colour you make is so full of transparency.
The instant something artificial happens, it can
shatter the atmosphere of the music.'

Trifonov has cherished memories of his previous
Proms performances, too. 'The moment I walked
on that stage, I was startled by the energetic
atmosphere and the massive space around you,
filled with thousands of listeners. It can take you
to another realm.'

THURSDAY 8 SEPTEMBER

PROM 72
7.00pm–c9.15pm • Royal Albert Hall

PRICE BAND **C** *Seats £14 to £58 (plus booking fee*)*

NIKOLAI ZNAIDER

Beethoven Violin Concerto in D major   45'

INTERVAL

Reger Variations and Fugue on
a Theme by Mozart   34'

Strauss
Till Eulenspiegels lustige Streiche   15'

Nikolaj Znaider *violin*

Staatskapelle Dresden
Christian Thielemann *conductor*

The Staatskapelle Dresden and its Chief Conductor
Christian Thielemann open with Beethoven's most
radiant, smiling work, his sublime Violin Concerto,
in the sure hands of Nikolaj Znaider. After the
interval this famously rich-toned orchestra digs
into Max Reger's affectionate and beautifully
orchestrated *Variations and Fugue on a Theme
by Mozart* and finally Richard Strauss's witty
and abrasive depiction of an impish figure from
German folklore, his outlandish tone-poem telling
of 'Till Eulenspiegel's merry pranks'.

RADIO *Live on BBC Radio 3*
ONLINE *Listen and catch up at bbc.co.uk/proms*

PROMS EXTRA
5.15pm–6.00pm • Imperial College Union BBC Radio 3
presenter Ian MacMillan, award-winning poet Jackie Kay
and Director of The Poetry Society Judith Palmer introduce
the winning entries in this year's BBC Proms Poetry
Competition and welcome some of the winners on stage
to read their poems. *In association with The Poetry Society.
Edited version broadcast on BBC Radio 3 after tonight's Prom*

THURSDAY 8 SEPTEMBER

PROM 73
10.15pm–c11.30pm • Royal Albert Hall

PRICE BAND **E** *£7.50 to £25 (plus booking fee*)*

RICARD EGARR

Handel Zadok the Priest   6'

Handel My heart is inditing   12'

Muffat Armonico tributo –
Sonata No. 5 in G major   22'

Handel Let thy hand be strengthened   8'

J. S. Bach, arr. L. Stokowski
Orchestral Suite No. 3 in D major,
BWV 1068 – Air   5'

Purcell, arr. L. Stokowski
Dido and Aeneas –'When I am laid in
earth' (Dido's Lament)   5'

Handel The King shall rejoice   11'

Academy of Ancient Music
Richard Egarr *conductor*

On 11 October 1727, George II was crowned
King of England at Westminster Abbey. The House
of Hanover's favourite composer was the natural
choice to provide the music. Handel wrote four
majestic Coronation Anthems for the occasion,
the most famous, *Zadok the Priest*, designed to
unleash its blazing choral entry just as George
stepped into the Abbey's chancel. The Academy
of Ancient Music returns to the Proms to fill the
Royal Albert Hall with all the regal splendour of
Handel's Coronation Anthems and with Leopold
Stokowski's equally grandiose upholstering of music
by Bach and Purcell.

RADIO *Live on BBC Radio 3*
ONLINE *Listen and catch up at bbc.co.uk/proms*

FRIDAY 9 SEPTEMBER

PROM 74
7.30pm–c9.10pm • Royal Albert Hall

PRICE BAND **C** *Seats £14 to £58 (plus booking fee*)*

TAMARA WILSON

Verdi Requiem   86'

Tamara Wilson *soprano*
Alisa Kolosova *mezzo-soprano*
Michael Fabiano *tenor*
Morris Robinson *bass*

BBC Proms Youth Choir
Orchestra of the Age of Enlightenment
Marin Alsop *conductor*

There will be no interval

Verdi's shattering *Requiem* – which began life as
a memorial to Rossini – was so forthright in its
expression of grief, faith and judgement that
many thought it too dramatic for performance
in church. In the penultimate Prom of 2016,
Marin Alsop leads the period instruments of
the Orchestra of the Age of Enlightenment and
the fresh voices of the BBC Proms Youth Choir
through all the passion, turbulence and reflection
of Verdi's sacred masterpiece. See 'Theatre in the
Blood', pages 24–27; 'Nurturing Talent', pages 72–73.

RADIO *Live on BBC Radio 3*
TV *Broadcast on BBC Four this evening*
ONLINE *Listen, watch and catch up at bbc.co.uk/proms*

PROMS EXTRA
5.45pm–6.30pm • Imperial College Union Join Director of
the Proms David Pickard and Chris Cotton, Chief Executive
of the Royal Albert Hall, as they look back over the 2016
Proms season.

George Longe (Znaider); Marco Borggreve (Egarr); Tamara Wilson (Wilson)

6–9 SEPTEMBER

BBC Last Night of the Proms

SATURDAY 10 SEPTEMBER

PROM 75 • THE LAST NIGHT OF THE PROMS 2016

7.15pm–c10.30pm • Royal Albert Hall

PRICE BAND G *Seats £27 to £97 (plus booking fee*)*

JUAN DIEGO FLÓREZ

Tom Harrold Raze — c5'
BBC commission: world premiere

Butterworth
The Banks of Green Willow — 7'

Borodin
Prince Igor – Polovtsian Dances — 12'

Rossini La Cenerentola –
'Sì, ritrovarla io guiro' — 6'

Donizetti L'elisir d'amore –
'Una furtiva lagrima' — 5'

Offenbach La belle Hélène –
'Au mont Ida' — 5'

Britten
Matinées musicales (after Rossini) — 10'

Jonathan Dove
Our revels now are ended — 8'

INTERVAL

Vaughan Williams
Serenade to Music — 11'

Donizetti La fille du régiment –
'Ah! mes amis' — 7'

Latin American medley — 8'

Elgar
Pomp and Circumstance March No. 1
in D major ('Land of Hope and Glory') — 8'

arr. Wood
Fantasia on British Sea-Songs — 15'

Arne, arr. **Sargent** Rule, Britannia! — 5'

Parry, orch. **Elgar** Jerusalem — 3'

The National Anthem (arr. Britten) — 3'

Trad., arr. **Thorpe Davie**
Auld Lang Syne — 2'

Juan Diego Flórez *tenor*

**Francesca Chiejina, Eve Daniell,
Lauren Fagan, Alison Rose** *sopranos*

**Claire Barnett-Jones, Marta
Fontanals-Simmons, Anna Harvey,
Katie Stevenson** *mezzo-sopranos*
**Trystan Llŷr Griffiths, Oliver Johnston,
Joshua Owen Mills, James Way** *tenors*
**Bragi Jónsson, Benjamin Lewis,
James Newby, Bradley Travis** *basses*

BBC Proms Youth Ensemble
BBC Singers
BBC Symphony Chorus
BBC Symphony Orchestra
Sakari Oramo *conductor*

Peruvian tenor Juan Diego Flórez is the star soloist in a Last Night that also showcases a hand-picked selection of young singers in Vaughan Williams's *Serenade to Music*. See 'Theatre in the Blood', pages 24–27; 'Nurturing Talent', pages 72–73; 'New Music', pages 86–95; 'Parry's "Jerusalem"', pages 100–101.

RADIO *Live on BBC Radio 3*
TV *First half live on BBC Two, second half live on BBC One*
ONLINE *Listen, watch and catch up at bbc.co.uk/proms*

PROMS EXTRA
4.30pm–5.45pm • Imperial College Union As the 2016 BBC Proms season draws to a close, join us for an edition of BBC Radio 3's *The Choir*, featuring a celebration of the centenary of Parry's *Jerusalem*, with Sara Mohr-Pietsch. *Tickets available from BBC Studio Audiences: bbc.co.uk/showsandtours/shows. Broadcast live on BBC Radio 3*

BBC Proms IN THE PARK

SATURDAY 10 SEPTEMBER

THE ROYAL PARKS

PROMS IN THE PARK
Gates open 3.00pm • Entertainment from 5.15pm • Hyde Park, London

Standard Admission Tickets £40 (plus booking fee*)

PAUL O'GRADY

Juan Diego Flórez *tenor*
Paul O'Grady *presenter*

BBC Concert Orchestra
Richard Balcombe *conductor*

Artists to include:
Cast from Matilda: The Musical

Join in the Last Night of the Proms celebrations in Hyde Park, hosted by Paul O'Grady. The open-air concert features a host of musical stars, including Proms in the Park favourites the BBC Concert Orchestra under the baton of Richard Balcombe, and special guest Juan Diego Flórez, who will also appear across the road at the Royal Albert Hall.

We also celebrate the centenary year of author Roald Dahl with a performance of *Matilda: The Musical* from the Royal Shakespeare Company's multi-award-winning West End production.

Listen to BBC Radio 2 from Monday 2 May for announcements of headline artists and special guests.

RADIO *Live on BBC Radio 2*
TV *Highlights from all of the Proms in the Park concerts on the red button*
ONLINE *Listen, watch and catch up at bbc.co.uk/proms*

BOOKING TICKETS
Tickets available from 11.00am on Friday 6 May from the Royal Albert Hall.
Ticket requests may also be included in the Proms Planner submitted from 9.00am on Saturday 7 May. See below for details of how to book.

ONLINE bbc.co.uk/promsinthepark
BY PHONE
from the **Royal Albert Hall** on **0845 401 5040** †
(a booking fee of 2% of the total value plus £2.00 per ticket up to a maximum of £25.00 applies for telephone bookings)

IN PERSON at the Royal Albert Hall Box Office
(no fees apply to tickets bought in person)

BY POST see page 152

For details of how to order a picnic hamper for collection on the day, or to find out about VIP packages and corporate hospitality, visit bbc.co.uk/promsinthepark

PLEASE NOTE In the interest of safety, please do not bring glass items (including bottles), barbeques or flaming torches to the event.

EXPERIENCE THE LAST NIGHT MAGIC AROUND THE UK!

HYDE PARK, LONDON
NORTHERN IRELAND
SCOTLAND
WALES

The **BBC Proms in the Park** events offer live concerts featuring high-profile artists, well-loved presenters and **BBC Big Screen** link-ups to the Royal Albert Hall, when you can join with audiences across the nations. So gather your friends and your Last Night spirit for an unforgettable evening.

Keep checking bbc.co.uk/promsinthepark for announcements of artists, venue and booking information.

Highlights of the Last Night celebrations around the UK will feature as part of the live television coverage of the Last Night and you can watch more at bbc.co.uk/proms.

You can also access Proms in the Park content via the red button.

10 SEPTEMBER

TICKET PRICES

ROYAL ALBERT HALL

A wide variety of seated tickets are available for all BBC Proms concerts at the Royal Albert Hall, as well as hundreds of Promming (standing) places in the Arena and Gallery. RAH concerts fall into one of eight price bands, indicated below each concert listing on pages 111–149.

PROMMING

Standing places are available in the Arena and Gallery on the day for £6.00.

Save by buying a Weekend Promming Pass, or a Whole- or Half-Season Promming Pass, available from 9.00am on Thursday 5 May (see page 155).

	A	B	C	D	E	F	G	H
Grand Tier Boxes 12 seats, price per seat	£38.00	£48.00	£58.00	£68.00	£25.00	£35.00	£97.00	£20.00
	(As most Grand Tier Boxes are privately owned, availability is limited)							
Loggia Boxes 8 seats, price per seat	£34.00	£44.00	£54.00	£64.00	£25.00	£35.00	£92.00	£20.00
2nd Tier Boxes 5 seats, price per seat	£30.00	£40.00	£50.00	£60.00	£25.00	£35.00	£89.00	£20.00
Centre Stalls	£30.00	£40.00	£50.00	£60.00	£20.00	£30.00	£89.00	£16.00
Side Stalls	£28.00	£38.00	£48.00	£58.00	£20.00	£30.00	£87.00	£16.00
Mid Choir	£20.00	£25.00	£34.00	£44.00	£20.00	£30.00	£65.00	£16.00
Upper Choir	£18.00	£22.00	£29.00	£37.00	£15.00	£20.00	£62.00	£12.00
Front Circle	£17.00	£20.00	£24.00	£29.00	£15.00	£20.00	£58.00	£12.00
Rear Circle	£12.50	£15.50	£19.50	£24.50	£15.00	£20.00	£47.00	£12.00
Restricted View Circle	£7.50	£9.50	£14.00	£18.00	£7.50	£10.00	£27.00	£7.50

Please note: a booking fee of 2% of the total value (plus £2.00 per ticket up to a maximum of £25.00) applies to all bookings (including Season and Weekend Promming Passes), other than those made in person at the Royal Albert Hall.

TICKET PRICES & DISCOUNTS

UNDER-18s GO HALF-PRICE

The Proms are a great way to discover live music and we encourage anyone over 7 years old to attend. Tickets for persons aged 18 and under can be purchased at half price in any seating area for all Proms except the Last Night (Prom 75) and in any price band except for £6.00 tickets at any venue. This discount is available through all booking methods.

GREAT SAVINGS FOR GROUPS

Groups of 10 or more attending concerts at the Royal Albert Hall can claim a 10% discount (5% for C-band and D-band concerts) on the price of Centre/Side Stalls or Front/Rear Circle tickets (excluding the Last Night), subject to availability.

Please note: group bookings can only be made by phone or in person at the Royal Albert Hall. To make a group booking, or for more information, call the Group Booking Information Line on 020 7070 4408 (from 9.00am on Saturday 7 May).

TICKETS AND DISCOUNTS FOR DISABLED CONCERT-GOERS

All disabled concert-goers (and one companion) receive a 50% discount on all ticket prices (except Arena and Gallery areas) for concerts at the Royal Albert Hall and Cadogan Hall. To claim this discount, call the **Access Information Line 020 7070 4410** (from Saturday 7 May) if booking by phone. Note that discounts for disabled concert-goers cannot be combined with other ticket offers.

Tickets can also be purchased in person from 9.00am on Saturday 7 May at the Royal Albert Hall. The Box Office has ramped access, an induction loop and drop-down counters.

Ambulant disabled concert-goers (disabled concert-goers who do not use a wheelchair) can also book tickets online from 9.00am on Saturday 7 May and use the online Proms Planner from 2.00pm on Wednesday 13 April (see page 152).

Please note that wheelchair spaces cannot be booked online or via the Proms Planner.

See pages 162–163 for Access Information for all venues.

CADOGAN HALL PROMS CHAMBER MUSIC

Stalls: £14.00, Centre Gallery: £12.00, Day Seats: £6.00 (booking fees apply)

Cadogan Hall tickets are available to book from 9.00am on Saturday 7 May and may be included in the Proms Planner (see page 152).

From Saturday 14 May Cadogan Hall tickets can also be bought direct from Cadogan Hall (020 7730 4500) as well as from the Royal Albert Hall Box Office. All online and telephone bookings made through the Cadogan Hall Box Office are subject to a fee of £3.00 per transaction.

On the day of the concert, tickets can be bought at Cadogan Hall only – from 10.00am. At least 150 Day Seats (Side Gallery bench seats) are available from 10.00am on the day of the concert. They must be purchased in person, with cash only, and are limited to two tickets per transaction.

Save by buying a Proms Chamber Music Series Pass, available from 9.00am on Thursday 5 May (see page 157 for details).

Unwanted tickets for all Proms that have been purchased through the Royal Albert Hall Box Office may be exchanged for tickets to other Proms concerts (subject to availability). A fee of £1.00 per ticket will be charged for this service. Call the Royal Albert Hall Box Office (0845 401 5040†) for further details.

BBC PROMS IN THE PARK, HYDE PARK, LONDON SATURDAY 10 SEPTEMBER

Tickets (standard admission) £40.00

A booking fee of 2% of the total value (plus £2.00 per ticket up to a maximum of £25.00) applies, unless booking in person at the Royal Albert Hall. See page 149 for details on how to book.

'PROMS AT …' MATINEES

Tickets for the 'Proms at …' matinees are available to book from 9.00am on Friday 24 June from the Royal Albert Hall Box Office.

Please note that these concerts are not included in the Proms Planner. Ticket prices are listed below. For Promming tickets, see page 157.

A booking fee of 2% of the total value (plus £2.00 per ticket up to a maximum of £25.00) applies, unless booking in person at the Royal Albert Hall.

BOLD TENDENCIES MULTI-STOREY CAR PARK, PECKHAM

Reserved Seats: £12.00, Unreserved Seats and Standing Tickets: £6.00 (booking fees apply). Day tickets: £6.00

Tickets can only be bought in advance from the Royal Albert Hall Box Office. A limited number of standing places will also be available at the venue from 11.00am on the day (see page 157).

THE CHAPEL, OLD ROYAL NAVAL COLLEGE, GREENWICH

Unreserved Seats £14.00 (booking fees apply). Day Seats (Balcony): £6.00

Tickets can only be bought in advance from the Royal Albert Hall Box Office. A limited number of Promming places will also be available at the venue from 2.00pm on the day (see page 157).

ROUNDHOUSE, CAMDEN

Standing tickets: £6.00 (booking fees apply). Some day tickets available

From Friday 1 July Roundhouse tickets can also be bought from the Roundhouse Box Office as well as from the Royal Albert Hall Box Office. Please note: only standing places are available for this concert.

SAM WANAMAKER PLAYHOUSE

Seats: £14.00 (booking fees apply). Day Tickets (Upper Gallery Standing): £6.00

From 10.00am on Friday 1 July Sam Wanamaker Playhouse tickets can also be bought from Shakespeare's Globe (020 7401 9919) as well as from the Royal Albert Hall Box Office.

HOW TO BOOK

General booking opens on Saturday 7 May at 9.00am

Online at bbc.co.uk/proms or www.royalalberthall.com

By telephone on 0845 401 5040[†] (open 9.00am–9.00pm daily). From outside the UK, please call +44 20 7589 8212.

In person at the Royal Albert Hall Box Office

Tickets may also be requested **by post**.

Season and Weekend Promming Passes are available to purchase online, by phone and in person from 9.00am on Thursday 5 May.

Promming: for standing tickets in the Arena and Gallery, priced £6.00, see page 155.

Last Night of the Proms: owing to high demand, special booking arrangements apply to tickets: see opposite.

Tickets for the **Ten Pieces Proms** (Proms 10 & 12) and **CBeebies Proms** (Proms 56 & 58) are available to purchase online, by phone and in person from 9.00am on Friday 6 May. Please note that these concerts are not part of the Proms Planner.

Proms in the Park: for tickets, see page 149.

'Proms at …' matinees: tickets available from 9.00am on Friday 24 June.

ONLINE

Wednesday 13 April (2.00pm) to Friday 6 May (midnight)

Use the **Proms Planner**, accessible via bbc.co.uk/proms to create your personal Proms Plan. Once completed, this is ready for you to submit as soon as general booking opens at 9.00am on Saturday 7 May. Submitting your Proms Plan as soon as booking opens speeds up the booking process and means that you may be more successful in securing your preferred tickets for concerts in high demand. You can also pre-register your payment card to speed up the checkout process.

You must submit your Proms Plan in order to make a booking.

If you have any queries about how to use the Proms Planner, call the Royal Albert Hall Box Office on 0845 401 5040[†].

Should you not wish to use the Proms Planner, you can visit www.royalalberthall.com from 9.00am on Saturday 7 May to book your tickets online.

Please note: it is not possible to book entire boxes online. If you would like to book a full box, call the Box Office on 0845 401 5040[†] from 9.00am on Saturday 7 May.

The 'Select Your Own Seat' option is not available via the Proms Planner or during the first few days that Proms tickets are on sale. You will be allocated the best available places within your chosen seating area. This is to allow as many customers as possible to book as efficiently as possible during the period of high demand.

From 9.00am on Saturday 7 May

From 9.00am on Saturday 7 May you can book online at **www.royalalberthall.com**.

Please note that the website will experience very high demand for tickets that day, so you will be placed in a queue. **Please use a secure connection to maintain your place in the queue.**

If you already have a Proms Plan, you can redeem your plan and submit your booking. If you do not have a Proms Plan, you can just book online.

A booking fee of 2% of the total value (plus £2.00 per ticket up to a maximum of £25.00 per booking) applies.

BY TELEPHONE

From 9.00am on Saturday 7 May, call the Royal Albert Hall Box Office on 0845 401 5040[†] (open 9.00am–9.00pm daily). From outside the UK, please call +44 20 7589 8212.

A booking fee of 2% of the total value (plus £2.00 per ticket up to a maximum of £25.00 per booking) applies.

IN PERSON

From 9.00am on Saturday 7 May, visit the Royal Albert Hall Box Office at Door 12. (Open 9.00am–9.00pm daily.)

No booking fees apply to tickets bought in person.

BY POST

Please write to BBC Proms, Box Office, Royal Albert Hall, London SW7 2AP with the following details:

- your name, address, telephone number(s) and email address (if applicable)
- the concerts you wish to attend
- number of tickets required
- preferred seating section, preferably with alternatives (see *ticket prices and seating plan on pages 150–151*)
- applicable discounts (see page 151)
- a cheque, payable to 'Royal Albert Hall' and made out for the maximum amount (including booking fees); or your credit card details, including type of card, name on the card, card number, issue number (Maestro only), start date, expiry date and security code (last three digits on back of Visa/Mastercard or last four digits on front of American Express).

Your details will be held securely.

General postal bookings will start to be processed from 9.00am on Saturday 7 May, when booking opens.

Postal bookings for Season and Weekend Promming Passes must be made separately to other booking requests. Please mark your envelope 'Proms Season Pass' or 'Weekend Pass' as appropriate. These bookings will be processed from 9.00am on Thursday 5 May.

Please note: following the start of booking, all postal applications are processed in random order, not the order in which they are received.

A booking fee of 2% of the total value (plus £2.00 per ticket up to a maximum of £25.00 per booking) applies.

[†] *Calls cost up to 5p/min from most landlines (an additional connection fee may also apply). Calls from mobiles may cost considerably more. All calls will be recorded and may be monitored for training and quality-control purposes.*

THE LAST NIGHT OF THE PROMS

Owing to high demand, the majority of tickets for the Last Night of the Proms are allocated by ballot to customers who have bought tickets to at least five other Proms concerts at the Royal Albert Hall. A further 200 tickets will be allocated by the Open Ballot (see far right).

The Five-Concert Ballot

Customers who purchase tickets for at least five other concerts at the Royal Albert Hall are eligible to enter the Five-Concert Ballot. You can apply to buy a maximum of two tickets for the Last Night. If you are successful in the Ballot, you will not be obliged to buy Last Night tickets should your preferred seating area not be available.

Please note: you must tick the Ballot opt-in box when booking online, or inform the Box Office that you wish to enter this Ballot when booking by telephone, in person or by post.

If you require a wheelchair space for the Last Night of the Proms, you will still need to book for five other concerts but you must phone the Access Information Line (020 7070 4410) by Thursday 26 May and ask to be entered into the separate Ballot for wheelchair spaces. This Ballot cannot be entered online.

The Five-Concert Ballot closes on Thursday 26 May. Successful applicants will be informed by Friday 3 June. If you are successful, **please note that your Last Night tickets will not be issued until Friday 2 September.** We regret that, if you are unsuccessful in the Five-Concert Ballot, no refunds for other tickets purchased will be payable.

GENERAL AVAILABILITY FOR THE LAST NIGHT

Any remaining tickets will go on sale on Friday 8 July at 9.00am, by telephone or online only. There is exceptionally high demand for Last Night tickets, but returns occasionally become available, so it is always worth checking with the Box Office.

Please note: for all Last Night bookings, only one application (for a maximum of two tickets) can be made per household.

PROMMING AT THE LAST NIGHT

Whole Season Promming Passes include admission to the Last Night.

A limited allocation of Last Night tickets (priced £6.00) is also reserved for Prommers who have attended five or more concerts (in either the Arena or the Gallery). They are eligible to purchase one ticket each for the Last Night (priced £6.00) on presentation of their used tickets (which will be retained) at the Box Office. Tickets will be available to buy from the Box Office from the following dates:

- Wednesday 20 July for First Half Season Pass-holders, Weekend Pass-holders and Day Prommers with five used tickets
- Wednesday 17 August for Second Half Season Pass-holders, Weekend Pass-holders and Day Prommers with five used tickets
- Friday 2 September for both First and Second Half Season Pass-holders, Weekend Pass-holders and Day Prommers with five used tickets.

On the Night A limited number of Promming tickets will be available on the Last Night itself (priced £6.00, one per person). No previous ticket purchases are necessary.

Queuing Please note that queuing locations for the Last Night of the Proms may differ from other Proms, but stewards will be on hand to assist you.

Whole Season Pass-holders are guaranteed entrance until 20 minutes before the concert.

Sleeping Out Please note that it is not necessary for Prommers with Last Night tickets to camp out overnight to secure their preferred standing place inside the Hall. Ticket-holders may add their name to a list at the Stage Door at the Royal Albert Hall from 4.00pm on Friday 9 September. They then need to return to the queue in list order by 10.00am on Saturday 10 September.

LAST NIGHT OF THE PROMS
2016 Open Ballot Form

One hundred Centre Stalls seats (priced £89.00* each) and 100 Front Circle seats (priced £58.00* each) for the Last Night of the Proms at the Royal Albert Hall will be allocated by Open Ballot. No other ticket purchases are necessary. Only one application (for a maximum of two tickets) may be made per household.
* booking fees apply (see page 150)

If you would like to apply for tickets by Open Ballot, please complete the official Open Ballot Form on the back of this slip and send it by post only – to arrive no later than Thursday 30 June – to:

**BBC Proms Open Ballot
Box Office
Royal Albert Hall
London SW7 2AP**

Note that the Open Ballot application is completely separate from other Proms booking procedures. Envelopes should be clearly addressed to 'BBC Proms Open Ballot' and should contain only this official Open Ballot Form. The Open Ballot takes place on Friday 1 July and successful applicants will be contacted by Thursday 7 July.

This form is also available to download from bbc.co.uk/proms; or call 020 7765 2044 to receive a copy by post.

Please note: if you are successful in the Five-Concert Ballot, you will not be eligible for Last Night tickets via the Open Ballot.

LAST NIGHT OF THE PROMS
2016 Open Ballot Form

Title _____ Initial(s) _____

Surname _____

Address _____

_____

_____

_____

Postcode _____

Country _____

Daytime tel. _____

Evening tel. _____

Mobile tel. _____

Email _____

_____

_____

Please indicate your preferred seating option ‡ (Booking fees apply, *see page 150*)

☐ I wish to apply for one Centre Stalls ticket (£89.00)

☐ I wish to apply for two Centre Stalls tickets (£178.00)

☐ I wish to apply for one Front Circle ticket (£58.00)

☐ I wish to apply for two Front Circle tickets (£116.00)

‡ *We cannot guarantee that you will be offered tickets in your preferred seating section. You will not be obliged to buy tickets outside your preference, but we regret we cannot offer alternatives.*

The personal information given on this form will not be used for any purpose by the BBC or the Royal Albert Hall other than this Ballot.

HOW TO PROM

HOW TO PROM

WHAT IS PROMMING?

The popular tradition of Promming (standing in the Arena or Gallery areas of the Royal Albert Hall) is central to the unique and informal atmosphere of the BBC Proms.

There are two standing areas: the **Arena**, the large space in the centre of the auditorium directly in front of the stage, which gives you the opportunity to get up close to the performers, and the **Gallery**, running round the top of the Hall, which has an incredible acoustic and a spectacular bird's-eye view of the stage. All spaces are unreserved (except on the Last Night, see page 153).

HOW TO PROM

Up to 1,350 standing places are available for each Proms concert at the Royal Albert Hall, although the capacity may vary for each Prom.

This year, for the first time, a limited number of Promming tickets will be available to book online between 9.00am and 12.00pm on the day of the concert. (See 'Online Booking' page 156 for details.)

Or just turn up and, if you are in doubt about where to go, Royal Albert Hall stewards will point you in the right direction. The traditionally low prices allow you to enjoy world-class performances for just £6.00 each (or even less with a Season or Weekend Promming Pass).

SEASON AND WEEKEND PROMMING PASSES

Frequent Prommers can save money by purchasing a Season Pass covering the whole Proms season at the Royal Albert Hall only, including the Last Night (but excluding the Ten Pieces II Proms, Proms 10 & 12, and the CBeebies Proms, Proms 56 & 58), or only the first or second half (ie Proms 1–37, excluding Proms 10 & 12, or Proms 38–74, excluding Proms 56 & 58 and the Last Night), or a Weekend Promming Pass. All Passes allow access to either the Arena or Gallery.

Season and Weekend Promming Pass-holders benefit from:

- guaranteed entrance (until 20 minutes before each concert)
- great savings – prices can work out at less than £5.50 per concert.

Please note: Season and Weekend Promming Pass-holders arriving at the Hall less than 20 minutes before a concert are not guaranteed entry and should join the back of the Day Queue.

All Season and Weekend Promming Passes are subject to availability.

Season and Weekend Promming Passes can be purchased from 9.00am on Thursday 5 May. These tickets cannot be planned online via the Proms Planner.

Season Passes are non-transferable and two passport-sized photographs must be provided before tickets can be issued. ID may be requested upon entry.

Whole-Season Passes include admission to the Last Night and Half-Season Pass-holders have special access to a reserved allocation of Last Night Tickets (see page 153).

Weekend Promming Passes must be purchased a minimum of two hours before the start of the first concert covered. Prices vary for each weekend depending on the number of concerts included – see box below.

Please note: you may purchase a maximum of four passes per weekend.

There is no Weekend Promming Pass covering Proms 74 and 75. Weekend Promming Passes are valid for concerts at the Royal Albert Hall only.

Pass	Concerts	Price
Whole Season 15 July – 10 September	**Proms 1–75** (excluding Proms 10, 12, 56 & 58)	£240.00
First Half 15 July – 12 August	**Proms 1–37** (excluding Proms 10 & 12)	£144.00
Second Half 13 August – 9 September	**Proms 38–74** (excluding Proms 56 & 58)	£144.00
Weekend 1	**Proms 1–3**	£16.50
Weekend 2	**Proms 9–13** (excluding Proms 10 & 12)	£16.50
Weekend 3	**Proms 18–22**	£27.50
Weekend 4	**Proms 27–31**	£27.50
Weekend 5	**Proms 37–39**	£16.50
Weekend 6	**Proms 45–48**	£22.00
Weekend 7 (including Bank Holiday Monday)	**Proms 54–59** (excluding Proms 56 & 58)	£22.00
Weekend 8	**Proms 65–68**	£22.00

Please note: a booking fee of 2% of the total value (plus £2.00 per ticket up to a maximum of £25.00) applies to all bookings other than those made in person at the Royal Albert Hall

HOW TO PROM

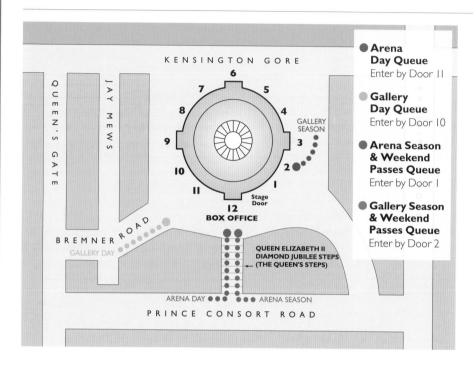

ONLINE BOOKING

This year, for the first time, a limited number of Arena and Gallery Promming tickets (priced £6.00) will be available on the day to purchase online between 9.00am and 12.00pm for main-evening and Late Night Proms.

Promming tickets for the Ten Pieces II Prom on Saturday 23 July (Prom 10) and the CBeebies Proms on Sunday 28 and Monday 29 August (Proms 56 & 58) will be available to purchase online the day before each concert between 9.00am and 12.00pm.

All Promming tickets purchased online are subject to a booking fee of 2% of the total value plus £1.00 per ticket. Tickets are limited to one per person, with the exception of the Ten Pieces II Proms (Proms 10 & 12) and the CBeebies Proms (Proms 56 & 58) for which four tickets per person will be available.

Promming tickets are available online for all Proms at the Royal Albert Hall (excluding the Last Night) and must be printed at home, or the PDF presented on your smartphone.

Prommers who have purchased tickets online should join the relevant Arena or Gallery Season queue, as shown on the map above, and are guaranteed entry only until the concert starts.

Prommers who purchase tickets online can also request a Seat Reservation Card by telephone (see *opposite* for details).

QUEUING

Prommers should join the relevant Arena or Gallery Day or Season queue, as shown on the map above. Stewards will be on hand to assist Prommers from 9.00am.

DAY PROMMERS

All remaining Arena and Gallery Promming tickets (priced £6.00) are available on the day and can be purchased in person with cash or, for the first time this year, contactless payment card, as well as online between 9.00am and 12.00pm (see 'Online Booking', *right*, for details).

The number of Promming tickets available is dependent on capacity and the number of Pass-holders in attendance; however, over 500 Arena and Gallery tickets are usually available, so you always have a good chance of getting in (although early queuing is advisable for the more popular concerts). Please see map (*above*) for queue locations. Ticket purchases are made as you enter, in queue order, through the relevant doors.

A limited number of Arena tickets will usually be sold to the Day Queue from two and a half hours before each performance (one and a quarter hours before Proms 10, 56 & 58). The remaining Day Promming tickets will then be sold from Door 11 (Arena) and Door 10 (Gallery) from 45 minutes before the performance to those queuing.

Tickets for Late Night Proms are available on the doors from 30 minutes before the performance. Arena and Gallery tickets are available only at Door 11 and Door 10, not at the Box Office.

HOW TO PROM

PROMMING TICKETS FOR WHEELCHAIR-USERS

The Gallery can accomodate up to four wheelchair-users. On arrival at the Royal Albert Hall, ask a steward for assistance. Wheelchair-users will be issued a queue number and can leave and return in time for doors opening, at which point all Prommers will enter in queue order. Please note that the Arena is not accessible to wheelchair-users.

PROMMING TICKETS FOR AMBULANT DISABLED CONCERT-GOERS

Up to 25 seats in the Arena and up to 36 seats in the Gallery will be available for reservation each day by ambulant disabled concert-goers (disabled concert-goers who do not use a wheelchair) who wish to Prom.

On arrival at the Royal Albert Hall, ambulant disabled concert-goers wishing to Prom that day should ask a steward (on duty from 9.00am) for a **Seat Reservation Card**, along with a queue number. You can then leave the queue, returning in time for doors opening (*see page 158*), at which point you can purchase your ticket as Prommers begin to enter the Hall queue order. If you secure a Promming ticket with a Seat Reservation Card, a seat will have been reserved for you.

Ambulant disabled Season and Weekend Promming Pass-holders and Online Promming ticket-holders can also make reservations for an allocation of seats in either the Arena or Gallery. Reservations (one per call) can be made between 9.00am and 12.00pm on the day of the concert by telephone only. Please call 020 7070 4410 to request a Seat Reservation Card, which you will need to collect from the Box Office before joining the queue for that day's Prom.

After 12.00pm reservations may be made in person only – please ask a steward for a Seat Reservation Card along with a queue number. You must be in the queue, having collected your Seat Reservation Card, no less than 20 minutes before the concert to guarantee entry, and a seat will have been reserved for you.

Please note: a Seat Reservation Card does not guarantee entry on its own – you must also purchase a Promming ticket.

CADOGAN HALL
PROMS CHAMBER MUSIC SERIES PASS

Hear all eight Monday-lunchtime Proms Chamber Music concerts for just £36.00 (plus £3.00 booking fee per transaction), with guaranteed entrance to the Side Gallery until 12.40pm (after which Proms Chamber Music

Series Pass-holders may be asked to join the Day Queue). Passes can be purchased from 9.00am on Thursday 5 May online, by phone or in person at the Royal Albert Hall. Two passport-sized photographs must be provided.

Please note: Proms Chamber Music Series Passes cannot be purchased from Cadogan Hall. Proms Chamber Music Series Passes are subject to availability.

'PROMS AT …' MATINEES

Promming tickets for the 'Proms at …' matinees are available on the day from each venue as detailed below.

Tickets are limited to two tickets per transaction.

BOLD TENDENCIES MULTI-STOREY CAR PARK, PECKHAM

Day Tickets (Standing): £6.00

A limited number of Promming tickets are available for cash only on the day from 11.00am (for the first performance) and from 12.00pm (for the second performance) at Bold Tendencies Multi-Storey Car Park.

THE CHAPEL, OLD ROYAL NAVAL COLLEGE, GREENWICH

Day Tickets: £6.00

A limited number of Promming tickets are available for cash only on the day from 2.00pm at the Box Office, situated in the Queen Mary Undercroft, beneath the Chapel.

ROUNDHOUSE, CAMDEN

Day Tickets (Standing): £6.00

A limited number of Promming tickets are available on the day from 12.00pm at the Roundhouse Box Office.

SAM WANAMAKER PLAYHOUSE

Day Tickets (Standing): £6.00

A limited number of Promming tickets are available on the day from 10.00am at Shakespeare's Globe Box Office.

Chris Christodoulou/BBC

BOOKING INFORMATION

ROYAL ALBERT HALL   Kensington Gore, London SW7 2AP *(see map opposite)* www.royalalberthall.com

FOOD AND DRINK
AT THE ROYAL ALBERT HALL

With a number of restaurants and bars, as well as box catering, there is a wide range of food and drink to enjoy at the Royal Albert Hall, from two and a half hours before each concert.

Booking in advance is recommended. Visit www.royalalberthall.com or call the Box Office on 0845 401 5040† to make your reservation.

BARS are located throughout the building, and open two hours before each concert.

INTERVAL DRINKS are available from any bar and, to beat the queues, you can order before the concert.

RESTAURANTS

Verdi – Italian Kitchen offers classics such as stone-baked pizza, pasta and mozzarella-topped fare. (First Floor, Door 12)

Elgar Bar & Grill serves meat, chicken and pork from the Josper Grill. All dishes are gluten-free. Set menu available. (Circle level, Door 9)

The Elgar Room will stay open late on 21 & 28 July, 4, 10, 18 & 25 August and 1 & 7 September for the informal Proms Extra Late events – see bbc.co.uk/proms for more information.

Coda Restaurant offers a two-course set menu, or French-influenced à la carte dishes. (Circle level, Door 3)

Cloudy Bay and Seafood Bar – enjoy light seafood and fish dishes alongside complementary wines. (Second Tier, Door 3)

Berry Bros. & Rudd No. 3 offers a selection of seasonal British dishes, sharing plates and salads. (Basement level, Doors 1 & 6)

Café Bar serves food and drink all day, including cakes, pastries, salads and sandwiches. The bar is open until 11.00pm. Free Wi-Fi available. (Ground Floor, Door 12)

GRAND TIER, SECOND TIER
AND LOGGIA BOX SEATS

If you have seats in one of the Royal Albert Hall's boxes, you can pre-order food and drinks to be served upon arrival or at the interval. The selection ranges from sandwiches and smoked salmon blinis to hot pies. Visit boxcatering. royalalberthall.com and please order at least 48 hours before the concert that you are attending.

Please note: the consumption of your own food and drink in the Hall is not permitted. Glasses and bottles are permitted in boxes, as part of box catering ordered through Rhubarb.

AUDITORIUM DOORS OPEN 45 minutes before the start of each concert (two and a half hours for restaurant and bar access) and 30 minutes before each late-night concert.

Tickets and passes will be scanned upon entry. Please have them ready, one per person.

LATECOMERS will not be admitted into the auditorium unless or until there is a suitable break in the performance.

BAGS AND COATS may be left in the cloakrooms at Door 9 (ground level) and at basement level beneath Door 6. A charge of £1.00 per item applies (cloakroom season tickets priced £20.40, including a 40p payment-handling fee, are also available). Conditions apply – see www.royalalberthall.com. For reasons of safety and comfort, only one small bag per person is permitted in the Arena.

SECURITY In the interests of safety, bags may be searched upon entry.

CHILDREN UNDER 5 are not allowed in the auditorium out of consideration for both audience and artists, with the exception of the Ten Pieces II Proms (Proms 10 & 12) and the CBeebies Proms (Proms 56 & 58).

DRESS CODE Come as you are: there is no dress code at the Proms.

PHONES AND RECORDING DEVICES, including mobiles, tablets and cameras are distracting to other audience members. Please ensure they are switched off. Recording is strictly forbidden.

'STORY OF THE PROMS' TOURS
OF THE ROYAL ALBERT HALL

Lasting approximately one hour and run throughout the Proms season. Other tours also run regularly For bookings and further information, including the Royal Albert Hall's other regular tours, call 0845 401 5045† or visit www.royalalberthall.com. For group bookings of 15 people or more, call 020 7959 0558. Special group rates apply.

PROMS AND ROYAL ALBERT HALL
GIFTS AND MERCHANDISE

Available inside the porches at Doors 6 and 12 and on the Circle level at Doors 4 and 8.

VENUE INFORMATION

Chris Christodoulou/BBC/RAH

GETTING THERE Royal Albert Hall & Imperial College Union

The nearest Tube stations are High Street Kensington (Circle & District Lines) and South Kensington (Piccadilly, Circle & District Lines). These are all a 10- to 15-minute walk from the Hall.

The following buses serve the Royal Albert Hall and Imperial College Union (via Kensington Gore, Queen's Gate, Palace Gate and/or Prince Consort Road): 9/N9, 10 (24-hour service), 49, 52/N52, 70, 360 & 452. Coaches 701 and 702 also serve this area.

The Royal Albert Hall has limited cloakroom space and may not be able to accept folding bicycles. Santander Cycles hire racks are positioned outside the Royal College of Art, the Royal College of Music and in Cadogan Place.

CAR PARKING

A limited number of parking spaces, priced £10.20 each (including a 20p payment-handling fee), are available from 6.00pm (or two hours before weekend matinee concerts) in the Imperial College car park. Entrances are located on Prince Consort Road (open daily until 7.00pm) and Exhibition Road. Vouchers are only valid until 45 minutes after the end of the concert. These can be booked online, by phone or in person at the Royal Albert Hall from 9.00am on Saturday 7 May, and planned online via the Proms Planner from 2.00pm on Wednesday 13 April. Please note that, if you are attending both early-evening and late-night concerts on the same day, only one parking fee is payable.

Please note: the Royal Albert Hall is not within the Congestion Charge zone.

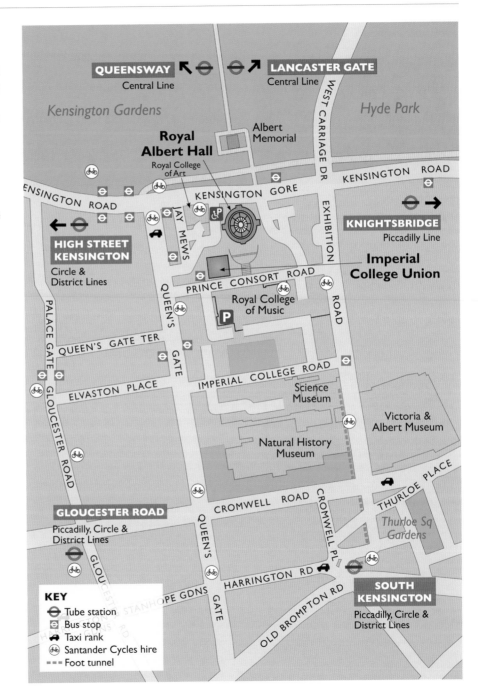

VENUE INFORMATION

CADOGAN HALL

5 Sloane Terrace, London SW1X 9DQ
www.cadoganhall.com

FOOD AND DRINK A selection of savouries, sandwiches and cakes is available from the Oakley Bar and Café. The café and bar will be open at 11.00am. Cadogan Hall's bars offer a large selection of champagne, wines, spirits, beer, soft drinks and tea and coffee.

DOORS OPEN at 11.00am (entrance to the auditorium from 12.30pm).

LATECOMERS will not be admitted unless or until there is a suitable break in the music.

BAGS AND COATS may be left in the cloakroom on the lower ground level. A charge of £1.00 per item applies.

CHILDREN UNDER 5 are not admitted to Cadogan Hall out of consideration for both audience and artists.

MOBILE PHONES and other electronic devices are distracting to other audience members. Please ensure they are switched off.

THE USE OF CAMERAS, video cameras and recording equipment is strictly forbidden.

GETTING THERE The following buses serve Cadogan Hall: 11, 19, 22, 137, 170, 211, 319, 360, 452 & C1.

CAR PARKING Please check street signs for details. Discounted car parking for Cadogan Hall performers and customers is available at the NCP Car Park, Cadogan Place, just 10 minutes' walk from Cadogan Hall. Parking vouchers are available on request from the Box Office.

IMPERIAL COLLEGE UNION

Prince Consort Road, London SW7 2BB *(see map, page 159)* www.imperialcollegeunion.org

PROMS EXTRA

Proms Extra pre-concert events will be held in the Concert Hall at Imperial College Union. Family Intros will be held in the Dining Hall in the same venue.

Proms Extra events are free of charge and unticketed (seating is unreserved), with the exception of the First Night live *In Tune* event on Friday 15 July, *The Listening Service* on Sunday 17 July, *The Choir* on Saturday 10 September and Radio 4's *Counterpoint* music quiz on Friday 2 September, for which free tickets will be available from BBC Studio Audiences (bbc.co.uk/showsandtours/shows). Places must be reserved in advance for all Proms Extra Family Orchestra & Chorus events and most Proms Extra Sing events (visit bbc.co.uk/proms or call 020 7765 0557).

Please note: seating at Imperial College Union is limited and all Proms Extra events are subject to capacity, so we advise arriving early for the more popular events. Latecomers will be admitted where possible but, as many of these events are recorded for broadcast, you may have to wait until a suitable break. The event stewards will guide you.

Prommers who join the Royal Albert Hall queue before the Proms Extra event should make sure they take a numbered slip from one of the Royal Albert Hall stewards to secure their place back in the queue.

If you have special access requirements, see the Imperial College Union information on page 162.

BOLD TENDENCIES MULTI-STOREY CAR PARK

95A Rye Lane, London SE15 4ST
www.boldtendencies.com

FOOD AND DRINK Frank's Cafe on Level 10 offers food and drink. There are no advance reservations, so we advise early arrival. Refreshments will also be available in the performance area.

DOORS OPEN 45 minutes before the performance.

LATECOMERS will not be admitted unless or until there is a suitable break in the music.

PERSONAL ITEMS and valuables are the responsibility of the visitor. There is no cloakroom available on site.

CHILDREN UNDER 5 are welcome, but parents are requested to show consideration to both artists and other audience members.

MOBILE PHONES and other electronic devices are distracting to other audience members. Please ensure they are switched off.

THE USE OF CAMERAS, video cameras and recording equipment is strictly forbidden.

GETTING THERE The following buses serve Bold Tendencies Peckham: 12, 37, 63, 78, 197, 343, 363, 484 & P12. Peckham Rye train station is a 5-minute walk from the car park.

CAR PARKING Limited parking is available on site via Cerise Road, off Hanover Park. Use the postcode SE15 5HQ for GPS devices. Paid parking is also available at Choumert Grove Car Park and on surrounding streets – please check street signs for details.

THE CHAPEL, OLD ROYAL NAVAL COLLEGE

Greenwich, London SE10 9NN
www.ornc.org

FOOD AND DRINK The Old Brewery, located next to the Discover Greenwich Visitor Centre, is a relaxed café during the day and a lively restaurant in the evening. There is also a bar that serves hand-drawn beers and a large al fresco courtyard.

DOORS OPEN one hour before the performance.

LATECOMERS will not be admitted unless or until there is a suitable break in the music.

BAGS AND COATS There is no cloakroom available on site. Personal items and valuables are the responsibility of the visitor.

CHILDREN UNDER 5 are not admitted out of consideration for both audience and artists.

MOBILE PHONES and other electronic devices are distracting to other audience members. Please ensure they are switched off.

THE USE OF CAMERAS, video cameras and recording equipment is strictly forbidden.

GETTING THERE The following buses serve the Old Royal Naval College: 129, 177, 180, 188, 199, 286 & 386. Greenwich Pier is a two-minute walk from from the Chapel and the DLR at Cutty Sark for Maritime Greenwich is a five-minute walk.

CAR PARKING There is no car parking available on site. The nearest public car parks can be found at Park Row, SE10 9NL and Cutty Sark Gardens, SE10 9HT.

ROUNDHOUSE, CAMDEN

Chalk Farm Road, London NW1 8EH
www.roundhouse.org.uk

FOOD AND DRINK The Made Bar & Kitchen at the Roundhouse is open from 10.30am daily for drinks and snacks and serves lunch, dinner on concert days and bottomless brunch at weekends.

Torquil's Bar and the Circle Bar overlook Chalk Farm Road and are open to everyone 30 minutes before the start of concert. The bars stay open throughout the performance and serve a great selection of drinks and snacks.

DOORS OPEN at 1.45pm (entrance to the auditorium 45 minutes before the performance).

LATECOMERS will not be admitted unless or until there is a suitable break in the music.

BAGS AND COATS may be left in the cloakroom on Level 0. A charge of £2.00 per coat and £3.00 per bag applies.

THE USE OF CAMERAS, video cameras and recording equipment is strictly forbidden.

GETTING THERE The nearest tube stations are Camden Town and Chalk Farm. Buses serving Chalk Farm Road include routes 24, 27, 31, 46, 168 & 393. Buses to and from Camden include routes 24, 27, 29, 31, 134, 135, 168, 214, 253, 274 & C2.

CAR PARKING There is no parking available at the Roundhouse, other than for Blue Badge holders (see Roundhouse access information on page 163).

Please note that only standing places are available for this concert. If you have any access requirements, please email access@roundhouse.org.uk.

SAM WANAMAKER PLAYHOUSE

Shakespeare's Globe, London SE1 9DT
www.shakespearesglobe.com

FOOD AND DRINK A selection of savouries, sandwiches and cakes and soft and alcoholic drinks is available from the Swan Bar (open from 9.30am–11.00pm) and Foyer Café Bar (open from 9.30am until after the evening interval). The Upper Foyer Bar will open one hour before the performance. The Swan Restaurant takes bookings on Saturdays between 12.00pm and 3.30pm and 6.00pm and 10.30pm.

DOORS OPEN at 9.00am (entrance to the auditorium 15 minutes before the performance).

LATECOMERS will not be admitted unless or until there is a suitable break in the music.

BAGS AND COATS may be left in the cloakroom on the lower ground level for a charge of £1.00. Large bags are not permitted in the auditorium.

CHILDREN UNDER 5 are not admitted to the auditorium.

MOBILE PHONES and other electronic devices are distracting to other audience members. Please ensure they are switched off.

THE USE OF CAMERAS, video cameras and recording equipment is strictly forbidden.

GETTING THERE The following buses serve Shakespeare's Globe: 11, 15, 17, 45, 23, 26, 63, 76, 100, 381, 344 & RV1. Bankside Pier is 10m/30ft from the theatre.

CAR PARKING There is an NCP car park on Thames Exchange on the north side of Southwark Bridge (open 24 hours, seven days a week).

theDPC (Greenwich); Will Pearson (Roundhouse); Pete le May (Sam Wanamaker)

VENUE INFORMATION

†SEE PAGE 152 FOR CALL-COST INFORMATION

ACCESS AT THE PROMS

ACCESSIBLE PRINT MATERIALS

- Audio CD and Braille versions of this Guide are available in two parts, 'Articles' and 'Concert Listings/Booking Information', priced £3.50 each. For more information and to order, call the RNIB Helpline on 0303 123 9999.

- A text-only large-print version of the Proms Guide is available, priced £7.00.

- Large-print concert programmes can be made available on the night (at the same price as the standard programme) if ordered not less than five working days in advance.

- Complimentary large-print texts and opera librettos (where applicable) can also be made available on the night if ordered in advance.

To order any large-print BBC Proms Guide, programmes or texts, please call 020 7765 3246. The programmes and texts will be left for collection at the Door 6 Information Desk 45 minutes before the start of the concert.

ROYAL ALBERT HALL

The Royal Albert Hall has a Silver award from the Attitude is Everything Charter of Best Practice. Full information on the facilities offered to disabled concert-goers (including car parking) is available online at www.royalalberthall.com. Information is also available through the Access Information Line, **020 7070 4410** (9.00am–9.00pm daily).

Provision for disabled concert-goers includes:

- 20 spaces bookable for wheelchair-users with adjacent companion spaces. For more details and to book call the Access Information Line

- six additional Side Stalls wheelchair spaces available for Proms 55–75

- seats available in the Arena and Gallery for reservation each day by ambulant disabled Prommers. For details see page 157

- ramped access, located at Doors 1, 3, 8, 9 and 12. For arrival by car, taxi, minibus or Dial-a-Ride, the most convenient set-down point is at Door 1, which is at the rear of the building and has ramped access.

- Public lifts located at Doors 1 and 8 with automatic doors, Braille and tactile numbering and voice announcements.

- Accessibility for wheelchair-users to all bars and restaurants.

Owing to development works, the Hall will not be able to offer parking for disabled concert-goers in its West Car Park this year. However, a limited number of spaces will be reserved close to the Hall; please contact the Access Information Line for more information.

Wheelchair spaces can be booked by calling the Access Information Line or in person at the Royal Albert Hall Box Office. For information on wheelchair spaces available for the Last Night of the Proms via the Five-Concert Ballot, see page 153.

Other services available on request are as follows:

- The Royal Albert Hall auditorium has an infra-red system with a number of personal headsets for use with or without hearing aids. Headsets can be collected on arrival from the Information Desk at Door 6.

- If you have a guide or hearing dog, the best place to sit in the Royal Albert Hall is in a box, where your dog may stay with you. If you prefer to sit elsewhere, stewards will be happy to look after your dog while you enjoy the concert.

- Transfer wheelchairs are available for customer use.

- A Royal Albert Hall steward will be happy to read your concert programme to you.

To request any of the above services, please call the Access Information line or complete an accessibility request form online at www.royalalberthall.com 48 hours before you attend. Alternatively you can make a request upon arrival at the Information Desk at Door 6 on the Ground Floor, subject to availability.

Following the success of the signed Proms in past years, a sign language interpreter will guide you through the Ten Pieces II Prom on Saturday 23 July (Prom 10) and the CBeebies Prom on Sunday 28 August (Prom 56). Tickets cost

between £12 and £20; disabled concert-goers (plus one companion) receive a 50% discount. Please book your tickets online in the usual way (see page 152). If you require good visibility of the signer, please choose the 'Stall Signer Area' online when selecting your tickets, or call the Access Information Line and request this area.

CADOGAN HALL

Cadogan Hall has a range of services to assist disabled customers, including:

- three wheelchair spaces in the Stalls available for advance booking and one space reserved for sale as a day ticket from 10.00am on the day of the concert. Please note: there is no lift access to the Gallery

- Box Office counter fitted with a loop system

- an infra-red amplification system in the auditorium. This is not the same as a loop system, so switching your hearing aid to 'T' is not sufficient. You will need to use an amplification aid.

Guide dogs are welcome to access the Hall and auditorium but please contact Cadogan Hall prior to arrival, so that any special arrangements can be made if necessary.

For further information, call 020 7730 4500.

IMPERIAL COLLEGE UNION

Imperial College Union has a range of services to assist disabled customers, including:

- a limited number of spaces for wheelchair-users in the Concert Hall and Dining Hall

- an induction loop installed in the Concert Hall

- step-free access from Prince Consort Road, located through Beit Quad.

If you require further assistance for your visit, contact the Beit Venues team on 07736 453 488 or email beitvenues@imperial.ac.uk.

ACCESS AT THE PROMS

BOLD TENDENCIES MULTI-STOREY CAR PARK, PECKHAM

There are no lifts available at Bold Tendencies Peckham, but the performance area can be accessed by wheelchairs via ramps from the ground floor.

If you require further assistance for your visit, email info@boldtendencies.com between 10.00am and 5.00pm, Monday to Friday.

THE CHAPEL, OLD ROYAL NAVAL COLLEGE, GREENWICH

There are two wheelchair spaces available at the Chapel, Old Royal Naval College. The Chapel is situated two floors above street level and access for wheelchair-users is via a manually driven Stairmate machine. The maximum person-wheelchair load is 200kg and maximum width is 69.5cm. The machine is not suitable for electric scooters. Please contact the Chapel in advance so that arrangements can be made.

Accessible toilets and the bar are four steps down from street level and can be accessed via ramp.

Parking is available for Blue Badge holders in the main car park, situated near the Chapel. These spaces should be booked in advance on 020 8269 4788.

If you require further assistance for your visit, contact us on 020 8269 4799 or email info@ornc.org.

ROUNDHOUSE, CAMDEN

The Roundhouse has a Gold award from the Attitude is Everything Charter of Best Practice. Full information on the facilities offered to disabled concert-goers (including car parking) is available online at www.roundhouse.org. Provision for disabled concert-goers includes:

- level access through power-assisted doors to the main entrance on Chalk Farm Road
- level access to the Main Space and bars and lifts providing access to all floors
- accessible toilets on all floors
- an infra-red amplification system in the Main Space, for which headsets are available at the Box Office. These can be used with or without a hearing aid
- Braille and tactile signage throughout the foyers.

Guide dogs are welcome at the Roundhouse and arrangements can be made to look after the dog during a performance. Water is available on request from the duty manager.

There are three parking spaces available for Blue Badge holders in the car park on Regents Park Road. These should be booked through www.roundhouse.org or by telephone: 0300 6789 222. The car park offers ramped access to Level 1 via the Stage Door.

If you require further assistance for your visit, contact the Roundhouse on 0300 6789 222 or email access@roundhouse.org.

SAM WANAMAKER PLAYHOUSE

The Sam Wanamaker Playhouse at Shakespeare's Globe has a range of services for disabled customers, including:

- level access to the Pit from New Globe Walk
- lift access to the Lower and Upper Galleries/ Swan Bar & Restaurant/Shop levels from New Globe Walk/Box Office foyer
- two wheelchair spaces, each with a companion seat if required, on the Lower Gallery
- hearing loop system.

Two parking spaces are available for disabled concert-goers, as well as limited parking spaces for Blue Badge holders on New Globe Walk and the surrounding area.

If you require further assistance for your visit, contact the Access Information Line on 020 7902 1409 between 10.00am and 5.00pm, Monday to Friday, or email access@shakespearesglobe.com.

INDEX OF WORKS

Bold italic figures refer to Prom numbers
PCM indicates Proms Chamber Music concerts at Cadogan Hall
BTMCP Bold Tendencies Multi-Storey Car Park, Peckham, Saturday 3 September
ORNC Old Royal Naval College, Greenwich, Saturday 6 August
RC Roundhouse, Camden, Saturday 20 August
SWP Sam Wanamaker Playhouse, Saturday 13 August
*first performance at a BBC Henry Wood Promenade Concert